The Psych 101 Series

James C. Kaufman, PhD, Series Editor

Department of Educational Psychology
University of Connecticut

Lesia M. Ruglass, PhD, is assistant professor of psychology at the City College of New York and a research scientist at the Trauma and Addictions Project. Her research interests center on the assessment and integrated treatment of posttraumatic stress disorder, substance use disorders, and reducing racial/ethnic disparities in mental health outcomes. Dr. Ruglass has authored or co-authored several peer-reviewed articles and presented her work at national and international conferences. She is currently member-at-large and co-chair of the Diversity and Multicultural Committee of Division 56 (Trauma Psychology) of the American Psychological Association. Dr. Ruglass also maintains a private practice in New York City.

Kathleen Kendall-Tackett, PhD, IBCLC, FAPA, is a health psychologist, international board-certified lactation consultant, and the owner and editor-in-chief of Praeclarus Press, a small press specializing in women's health. Dr. Kendall-Tackett is editor-in-chief of *Clinical Lactation*, a fellow of the American Psychological Association in Health and Trauma Psychology, president of the American Psychological Association's Division of Trauma Psychology, and editor-in-chief-elect of *Psychological Trauma*. She is a clinical associate professor of pediatrics at the Texas Tech University School of Medicine in Amarillo, Texas, and a research associate at the Crimes Against Children Research Center at the University of New Hampshire.

Dr. Kendall-Tackett specializes in women's health research, including breastfeeding, depression, trauma, and health psychology. She has written more than 390 articles or chapters and is the author or editor of 24 books on maternal depression, family violence, and breastfeeding. Her research interests include the psychoneuroimmunology of maternal depression and the lifetime health effects of trauma. Dr. Kendall-Tackett has won several awards for her work, including the Community Faculty Award from the Department of Pediatrics, Texas Tech University School of Medicine, and the 2011 John Kennell and Marshall Klaus Award for Excellence in Research from DONA International (with co-recipient Tom Hale). Her most recent books include *The Science of Mother–Infant Sleep* (2013), *Depression in New Mothers, Second Edition* (2010), and *The Psychoneuroimmunology of Chronic Disease* (2010). Her websites are UppityScienceChick.com, KathleenKendall-Tackett.com, and PraeclarusPress.com.

Psychology of Trauma

Trauma

101

Lesia M. Ruglass, PhD
Kathleen Kendall-Tackett,
PhD, IBCLC, FAPA

SPRINGER PUBLISHING COMPANY

NEW YORK

Springer Publishing Company, LLC
11 West 42nd Street
New York, NY 10036
www.springerpub.com

Acquisitions Editor: Nancy S. Hale
Composition: Amnet

ISBN: 978-0-8261-9668-2
e-book ISBN: 978-0-8261-9669-9

14 15 16 17 / 5 4 3 2 1

The author and the publisher of this Work have made every effort to use sources believed
to be reliable to provide information that is accurate and compatible with the standards
generally accepted at the time of publication. The author and publisher shall not be
liable for any special, consequential, or exemplary damages resulting, in whole or in
part, from the readers' use of, or reliance on, the information contained in this book.
The publisher has no responsibility for the persistence or accuracy of URLs for external
or third-party Internet websites referred to in this publication and does not guarantee
that any content on such websites is, or will remain, accurate or appropriate.

Library of Congress Cataloging-in-Publication Data

Ruglass, Lesia M., author.
 Psychology of trauma 101 / Lesia M. Ruglass, Kathleen Kendall-Tackett.
  p. ; cm.
 Includes bibliographical references and index.
 ISBN 978-0-8261-9668-2 (print : alk. paper) — ISBN 978-0-8261-9669-9 (e-book)
 I. Kendall-Tackett, Kathleen A., author. II. Title.
 [DNLM: 1. Stress Disorders, Post-Traumatic—psychology. 2. Stress
Disorders, Post-Traumatic—therapy. WM 172.5]
 RC552.P67
 616.85'21—dc23

                                                                    2014017751

Special discounts on bulk quantities of our books are available to corporations, professional associations, pharmaceutical companies, health care organizations, and
other qualifying groups. If you are interested in a custom book, including chapters
from more than one of our titles, we can provide that service as well.

For details, please contact:
Special Sales Department, Springer Publishing Company, LLC
11 West 42nd Street, 15th Floor, New York, NY 10036-8002
Phone: 877-687-7476 or 212-431-4370; Fax: 212-941-7842
E-mail: sales@springerpub.com

Printed in the United States of America by Gasch Printing.

Contents

CONTENTS

Acknowledgments

irst and foremost, I would like to thank my partner, Matthew Schumann, for his love, support, and editorial assistance throughout the writing of this book.

Special thanks to my family, Joan, Errol, Tracy, Shauna, Bryce, Zoe, Jodi, LJ, Cheryl, and Mike for their love, support, and encouragement. I've appreciated your being there to share in the happiness of completing this project.

Thanks to Tina, Tia, Silvia, Nathilee, and Laura for being wonderful friends and colleagues.

Thanks to my mentor and great friend Denise Hien. Your support and guidance throughout the years have been invaluable. Our work at the Trauma and Addictions Project at the City College of New York has been a continual source of growth and inspiration to me.

Many thanks to my co-author Kathy Kendall-Tackett. It was a pleasure collaborating and sharing the task of writing this book with you. Your enthusiasm, support, and guidance made the process an enjoyable one.

Finally, thanks to Nancy S. Hale for her insightful feedback and editorial suggestions.

—Lesia M. Ruglass

This book has been an interesting and enjoyable journey for me. I'd first like to thank my co-author, Lesia Ruglass, for agreeing to join me on this adventure. She has gladly shared the load of writing a book and has contributed much. Thank you for being such an able writing partner.

I'd also like to thank our editor, Nancy S. Hale, for seeing the potential in this project and guiding us every step of the way. We have both appreciated your guidance and encouragement throughout.

My business partner, Scott Sherwood, has helped tremendously, picking up the slack so many times when I needed to focus on writing. He has made it possible for me to continue to write while also building a small business. Thanks so much.

It would not have been possible to write (and finish!) a book without the help and support of my family. They have been there for me through many books, and my writing would not be possible without their support. Many thanks to my husband, Doug, and sons, Ken and Chris, for giving me the opportunity to step away from my everyday life to spend hours staring at my laptop screen.

—Kathleen Kendall-Tackett

Psychology of
Trauma
101

What Is Psychological Trauma?

Jenna was 14 years old when a fellow student, a young man named James, started paying attention to her. He periodically showed up at her house, wanting to talk. Jenna's father had never liked James, but Jenna was grateful that someone was interested in her. All of her friends had boyfriends, and she wanted one, too. She was thrilled when James finally asked her to go to the movies. He took her to a drive-in; during the movie, he raped her. After he was finished, as she sobbed in the passenger seat of his car, he asked whether she wanted something to eat. He then took her home as if nothing had happened. Several weeks after the assault, Jenna told a group of her astonished friends what had happened. Her friends were also 14 years old, and they didn't know what to say. It was the 1970s, and rape was not something people talked about.

Jenna had symptoms of posttraumatic stress disorder (PTSD) throughout high school and college; she was unable to go to sleep until almost dawn. Her symptoms dramatically affected her ability to perform at school. She suffered many physical symptoms as well, including chronic pain so severe that she made several trips to the emergency department. Doctors never identified the cause of Jenna's chronic health problems, but she did manage to reduce her symptoms using a variety of alternative health modalities. Jenna has managed to live her life, but her sexual assault has never been addressed.

April worked at a top finance firm in New York City. She earned a lot of money and was well regarded in her field. She traveled constantly but enjoyed the pace of her life, and she loved being able to do work that she did well.

When she became pregnant with her first child, she was elated. She assumed that she would handle the demands of birth and new motherhood with her normal aplomb. What she had not expected was the frightening ordeal she experienced at the hospital. She was stripped and exposed, overwhelmed by pain, completely shocked at the lack of care taken by the staff. She did not think she would survive the experience. She did survive—but nothing will ever be the same for her. She is truly questioning many of the assumptions she has held throughout her successful life. Where was the justice in what she experienced? Why hadn't she checked out the hospital and doctor more carefully? What could she have done differently? Why did her body fail her so miserably?

April just can't get the memories of her birthing experience out of her head. She is having trouble sleeping and feels disconnected from her baby. She wonders whether she will ever recover from the trauma she experienced at the hands of her medical providers.

Sam was a teenager when he was drafted into the army and sent to Vietnam. He was eventually captured by the Viet Cong and was a prisoner of war for 3 years. During his captivity, he was frequently tortured; somewhere along the way, he contracted hepatitis C. When he returned to the United States, he found that he needed to keep his service to his country secret—the Vietnam War was very unpopular at home. Years later, he continues to have nightmares about his experiences, and he suffers intrusive thoughts during the day.

Sam's health was also seriously compromised, largely by his hepatitis C. He experiences chronic pain and has frequently been subjected to painful medical testing, including regular liver biopsies. His chronic pain symptoms have continually triggered his PTSD. It took 2 years before he was finally approved within the Veterans Affairs system to receive pain medications, which his health care providers were reluctant to prescribe because of his PTSD. Only after his psychiatrist insisted that he be prescribed was Sam finally treated for chronic pain.

Sam's PTSD and health problems have detrimentally affected his family as well, leading to two divorces. After his second divorce, Sam moved to another state to be closer to his oldest son.

Sarah, a mother of three children, was in her early 20s when her town in her native Liberia was raided by rebel forces. Her father and brother were gunned down when they tried to stop soldiers from raping her. Afterward, the soldiers raped her. Sarah escaped to a refugee camp with one of her daughters, but even at the camp she never felt safe. She was eventually relocated to the United States with the daughter who stayed with her in the camp, but she was forced to leave two of her children behind in Liberia.

Sarah was sent to a state in northern New England, where the population was predominantly White. She speaks English, so she was able to get by. But the culture was so different. And she struggled as she tried to figure out how to live in a place where it seemed cold and dark most of the year. She misses her native country and the family she was forced to leave behind. But it is not safe for her to return.

WHAT ARE TRAUMATIC EVENTS?

Life as you know it can change in an instant. One day you are living your life. You're worried about getting all your tasks finished on your to-do list, being late for a meeting, or getting your car to start. The next thing you know, the bottom falls out of your world. It could be a street crime. A natural disaster might sweep through your city. Your child might be hit by a car. Or you might be diagnosed with a life-threatening illness. The hard reality is that traumatic events are remarkably common. In volume 2 of his seminal work *Trauma and Its Walk*, trauma pioneer Charles Figley said that an event will be troubling to the extent that it is "sudden, dangerous, and overwhelming." Almost three decades later, that description of traumatic events is as apt as ever.

There is confusion among the general population about what "traumatic" means. In popular parlance, people use the term not only to describe truly traumatic events, but also to describe events that are merely unpleasant (such as missing a plane). There is another, more technical definition of trauma. Psychological trauma can occur when a person experiences an extreme stressor that negatively affects his or her emotional or physical well-being. Trauma can cause emotionally painful and distressing feelings that overwhelm a person's capacity to cope and leave him or her with feelings of helplessness. Traumatic events can lead to PTSD and myriad other reactions, such as depression, substance abuse, sleep problems, and—potentially—chronic health problems, such as heart disease, diabetes, and cancer.

Individuals may directly experience a trauma, witness the trauma happen to someone else, or learn about a traumatic event happening to close family members or friends. According to the older definition of trauma in the *Diagnostic and Statistical Manual of Mental Disorders*, fourth edition, text revision (*DSM-IV-TR*, American Psychiatric Association [APA], 2000), an event is considered traumatic when it results in the actual or threatened injury or death of the person exposed to the trauma or in threat to the physical integrity of the person and when the person's emotional response to the traumatic event includes intense fear, helplessness, or horror.

With the advent of the new *DSM-5* (APA, 2013), the definition of what constitutes a traumatic event has changed. An event is considered traumatic if the event resulted in death or threatened death, actual or threatened physical injury, or actual or threatened sexual violation. The individual no longer needs to have had an intense emotional reaction to the experience—studies have shown that the emotions experienced at the time of or after trauma exposure (e.g., intense fear, helplessness, horror) are not necessarily predictive of later distress or mental health problems; thus they are no longer part of the definition of a traumatic event. The person could have directly experienced the event, witnessed the event, or learned of the event happening to a close friend or relative.

It was previously believed that exposure to trauma was outside the realm of normal human experience, but research has shown that traumatic events are quite common and can have long-lasting, even lifelong, consequences. Trauma exposure cuts across all walks of life, regardless of age, race, ethnicity, socioeconomic status, religion, and cultural background. Epidemiological studies estimate that approximately 30% to 80% of individuals living in the United States have been exposed to one or more traumatic events (Breslau, 2009; Kessler, Chiu, Demler, & Walters, 2005).

Psychological trauma can occur after exposure to a single event or multiple events compounded over time. The likely impact of a traumatic event is often determined by a variety of factors including individual, relational, and social and contextual variables, all of which work in concert to bring about resolution of the trauma. Some individuals have significant protective factors that promote resilience in the face of trauma exposure. Others experience immediate distress after the trauma, which resolves without intervention. Still others experience significant distress and difficulty recovering that result in lifelong functional impairment.

5

TYPES OF TRAUMATIC EVENTS

Although clinicians first started describing "shell shock" as early as World War I, PTSD is a relatively recent diagnosis, first becoming a formal diagnostic category in the third edition of the *DSM* (*DSM-III*; APA, 1980). Much of the work leading up to its inclusion in the *DSM-III* came from work with combat veterans, Holocaust survivors and their offspring, sexual assault survivors, and those who experienced political violence. More recently, medical events, such as a psychologically traumatic birth, cancer diagnosis, ICU stays, heart attack, or having a pre-term baby, were also recognized as causing trauma. What follows is a brief overview of the most common types of traumatic events that an individual might be exposed to during his or her lifetime.

Child Maltreatment

Child maltreatment, a multifaceted problem that occurs all over the world, includes the abuse and neglect of a child under the age of 18. According to the Child Abuse Prevention and Treatment Act (CAPTA, 2010), child maltreatment is

> any recent act or failure to act on the part of a parent or caretaker which results in death, serious physical or emotional harm, sexual abuse or exploitation; or an act or failure to act which presents an imminent risk of serious harm.

Physical abuse has been defined as nonaccidental physical acts that injure a child and may include behaviors such as punching, hitting, beating, or burning a child. Sexual abuse has been defined as attempted or completed sexual acts with a child (e.g., fondling or sexual intercourse) or sexual exploitation of a child through using the child for prostitution or child pornography. Emotional abuse (or psychological abuse) is a pattern of behavior that impairs a child's emotional development or sense of self-worth and may include behaviors such as harshly criticizing or denigrating the child (Cicchetti & Toth, 2005). Since there are often no overt signs of emotional abuse, it can be one of the most difficult forms of abuse to verify (Heim, Shugart, Craighead, & Nemeroff, 2010).

Exposure to domestic violence, parental substance abuse, and abandonment of a child are also seen as forms of child maltreatment. Physical, sexual, and emotional abuse all involve direct acts of violence against a child. In contrast, neglect (another form of child maltreatment) involves failure to take care of a child's basic needs (CAPTA, 2010; Mennen, Kim, Sang, & Trickett, 2010; Pereda, Guilera, Forns, & Gómez-Benito, 2009). Parents and caregivers are considered neglectful when they fail to provide for their children's shelter, food, clothing, emotional support, education, health care, and supervision.

Reported incidence rates of child maltreatment are generally assumed to poorly reflect the magnitude of the problem, because child victims may not readily admit their experiences due to feelings of shame, guilt, and continued dependence on the perpetrators (Pereda et al., 2009). The U.S. Department of Health and Human Services' (USDHHS) Children's Bureau's Child Maltreatment Report (2011) indicates that approximately 2 million cases of child maltreatment were reported and investigated during 2011, with 681,000 of those cases substantiated. Of substantiated cases, approximately 79% involved neglect, 15% involved physical abuse, and 10% involved sexual abuse. Children under age 1 had the highest rates of victimization, and racial and ethnic minority children were disproportionately represented among the victims. Tragically, in 2011, 1,545 children died as a result of child abuse and neglect (USDHHS Children's Bureau, 2011).

Studies indicate that maltreated children are typically exposed to multiple types of abuse that are chronic and unrelenting and that often lead to significant adverse physical and psychological outcomes throughout childhood and adulthood (Muela, de Arana, Barandiaran, Larrea, & Vitoria, 2012). Childhood maltreatment is

7

particularly devastating because it occurs during a neurobiologi-
cally vulnerable time period when the brain is still developing and
is more susceptible to harmful effects. Studies show that exposure
to child maltreatment may disrupt or alter normal brain development, which then places these individuals at increased risk for
later psychological and physical problems (Heim et al., 2010).

Some of the risk factors associated with child abuse and
neglect include individual factors, such as younger age, female
gender, and child physical disability; relationship factors, such
as negative parent–child interactions, particularly if the parent is
under high stress and has mental health/substance abuse problems of his or her own; environmental and community factors,
including poverty, social isolation, and poor neighborhood contexts; and social and cultural factors, including negative beliefs
about the rights of children and specific disciplinary practices
(Crosson-Tower, 2009).

Intimate Partner Violence/Domestic Violence

The Centers for Disease Control and Prevention (CDC, 2013)
define intimate partner violence (IPV) as "actual or threatened
physical, sexual, psychological or stalking violence by current or
former intimate partners (whether of the same sex or opposite
sex)." These various forms of IPV tend to co-occur. Epidemiological studies reveal that up to 12 million individuals are exposed to
IPV in any given year (CDC, 2013). Women experience IPV at an
alarmingly higher rate than men and suffer significantly greater
negative consequences.

The National Violence Against Women Survey (NVAWS)
revealed that approximately 20% of the women in the survey
(1 in 5 women) reported a lifetime history of physical assault
by their current or former partner, compared to only 7% of the
men in the survey (Tjaden & Thoennes, 2000). Moreover, women
reported a greater likelihood of being raped and stalked by intimate partners in their lifetime than men (4.5% versus 0.2% and
4.1% versus 0.5%, respectively; Tjaden & Thoennes, 2000). The

National Crime Victimization Survey (NCVS; Rennison & Welchans, 2000), revealed similar findings: Women reported victimization by their intimate partner at 5 times the rate of men and were more likely to be injured as a result of their victimization (50% versus 32%). A more recent survey conducted by the CDC, the National Intimate Partner and Sexual Violence Survey (NISVS; Black et al., 2011), underscored the ubiquity of violence in intimate relationships, with 1 in 4 women and 1 in 7 men reporting exposure to severe physical violence.

Although studies show that men and women are equally likely to perpetrate IPV (Ehrensaft, Moffitt, & Caspi, 2004; Finkel & Eckhardt, 2011), the frequency, duration, and consequences of IPV are significantly greater for women than men, with women experiencing more life threats, reporting greater fear of bodily harm and greater physical and psychological consequences—including injuries requiring medical treatment and the need for mental health services—as a result of their exposure to IPV (Breiding, Black, & Ryan, 2008; Rennison & Welchans, 2000). In 2007, IPV-related homicide was the cause of 2,340 deaths, of which women accounted for 64% of the fatalities.

These findings clearly indicate that women experience more negative consequences from IPV than men. It is also likely that these figures grossly underestimate the extent of the problem, as women are less likely to report exposure to IPV for fear that they will not be believed, to avoid the stigma of being a victim of IPV, and out of concern about the well-being of their partner (see Hien & Ruglass 2009, for review). Moreover, since the legal responses to IPV (arrests, prosecutions, orders of protection) are only moderately effective—with protective or restraining orders being routinely violated by 50% of the perpetrators—this leaves women at heightened risk for further victimization (Jordan, 2004).

The risk factors contributing to IPV are multifaceted and likewise include individual, relationship, community, and social factors. Individual-level risk factors may include childhood exposure to violence (witnessing IPV or being physically abused as a child), low self-esteem, younger age, social isolation, lower educational attainment, and unemployment. Relationship factors may include relationship conflict, low marital satisfaction, dysfunctional interaction patterns, financial problems, and impending separation or divorce. Community-level risk factors may include poverty and living in violent neighborhoods. Social factors may include traditional gender norms related to power and control and beliefs about the acceptability and appropriateness of violence (see Hien & Ruglass, 2009, for a comprehensive review).

When examining racial and ethnic differences in exposure to IPV, a more insidious picture emerges. The prevalence rates of IPV are greater among racial and ethnic minority women than in White women (Field & Caetano, 2005; Rennison & Welchans, 2000; Tjaden & Thoennes, 2000). For instance, Black females had a 35% higher reported rate of IPV than White women between 1993 and 1998 (Rennison & Welchans, 2000) and were more than 2.36 times more likely to report experiencing severe violence (Hampton & Gelles, 1994). Hispanic women reported a greater frequency of rapes and Native American women reported experiencing more physical violence (e.g., Tjaden & Thoennes, 2000) than White females. Finally, rates of IPV-related homicides were higher for Native Americans and Blacks than Whites in 2007 (2.1 and 1.6 per 100,000 population, respectively).

The disproportionately greater rate of exposure to IPV among racial and ethnic minority women is likely related to their overrepresentation among individuals who are of lower socioeconomic status (e.g., being poor, low educational attainment, limited or no access to health insurance and health or mental health services), a consequence of structural inequalities that persist in our society (e.g., Hampton, Oliver, & Magarian, 2003; West, 2004). Being from a lower socioeconomic status places one at a greater risk of experiencing interpersonal violence (Sorenson, Upchurch, & Shen, 1996).

The NCVS found that the typical characteristics of IPV victims between 1993 and 1998 were "being black, young, divorced or separated, earning lower incomes and living in urban areas" (Rennison & Welchans, 2000, p. 3). Consistent with these theories, racial and ethnic differences in IPV exposure either disappear (e.g., Walton-Moss et al., 2005) or decrease substantially when socioeconomic status and substance use are controlled for (Field & Caetano, 2004), suggesting that perceived differences related to race may be more likely due to the effects of additional contextual factors such as poverty, discrimination, or substance abuse history (Bent-Goodley, 2007; Field & Caetano, 2004).

Rape or Sexual Violence

While the definition of rape has evolved over the years and can vary from state to state, it is generally defined as any completed sexual penetration that is nonconsensual and perpetrated with the use of threats, coercion, or physical force, or when the individual involved is not able to provide consent through physical or mental incapacity (Briere & Scott, 2012). For example, if someone is unconscious or impaired physically or psychologically due to alcohol or drugs or has a cognitive limitation, that person is deemed incapable of consenting. The NISVS study estimates that approximately 1 in 5 women (18%) and 1 in 71 men (1%) have experienced adult rape (Black et al., 2011). Moreover, in the 12 months prior to the NISVS survey, 1.3 million women reported experiencing rape or sexual assault.

The CDC (2013) utilizes the term *sexual violence*, a broader term that encompasses completed rape, attempted (but not completed) rape, unwanted sexual contact, and sexual harassment. Exposure to rape or sexual violence is associated with a variety of short-term and long-term psychological and physical consequences, including unintended pregnancies, sexually transmitted infections, depression, and PTSD (Jordan, Campbell, & Follingstad, 2010).

Military Sexual Trauma

Military sexual trauma (MST) has received increased research and clinical attention over the past 2 decades with a rapid upsurge occurring since the recent military conflicts (i.e., Operation Enduring Freedom [OEF] and Operation Iraqi Freedom [OIF]). The U.S. Department of Veterans Affairs (USDVA, 2014) defines MST as unwanted "experiences of sexual assault or repeated, threatening acts of sexual harassment that a Veteran experiences during his/her military service." Prevalence estimates of MST vary depending on the methodology, sample, and definitions utilized. For example, in face-to-face interviews, estimates of MST range from 4% to 71% (Suris & Lind, 2008). Surveys conducted via telephone or mail reveal estimates of MST ranging from 17% to 30% (Suris & Lind, 2008).

As with other types of traumas, women are more likely to be exposed to MST than men. One in 5 women has been exposed to MST, compared to only 1 in 100 men (USDVA, 2014). However, because there are more men in the military than women, the actual numbers of men and women who experienced MST are about equal (Suris & Lind, 2008; USDVA, 2014). As with other types of traumas, these figures may underestimate the true nature of the problem since many veterans may not disclose their MST out of shame, fear of blame, or fear of retaliation—or simply because they were not asked. The USDVA, however, has implemented a national screening policy whereby every service member is asked directly about exposure to MST and offered referrals to free treatment services if indicated.

A recent comprehensive review of screening data for 125,729 returning OEF and OIF veterans who received primary or mental health care found that 15% of women and 0.7% of men reported a history of MST while on active duty (Kimerling et al., 2010). A study by Rowe, Gradus, Pineles, Batten, and Davison (2009) of female veterans who sought outpatient mental health trauma treatment found that approximately 70% of the women reported experiencing MST. MST is associated with a range of psychological and physical health consequences. The risk factors associated with MST are varied and include younger age, being of enlisted rank, and childhood history of sexual abuse or assault (Suris & Lind, 2008).

Sex Trafficking

The federal Victims of Trafficking and Violence Protection Act of 2000 (VTVPA, 2000) defines sex trafficking as

> the recruitment, harboring, transportation, provision, or obtaining of a person for the purpose of a commercial sex act where such an act is induced by force, fraud, or coercion, or in which the person induced to perform such act has not attained 18 years of age.

Sexual trafficking is a significant and growing worldwide problem. Estimates of sex trafficking are variable and change over time. However, recent estimates indicate that approximately 800,000 people are trafficked across international borders for commercial sexual activities annually, 80% of whom are women and girls and 50% of whom are under the age of 18 (Deshpande & Nour, 2013; U.S. State Department, 2013).

Most commonly, individuals are deceived, coerced, or forced into sex trafficking through various means, including the promise of a better life in another country, being sold into the trade by their poor parents, or being kidnapped (Deshpande & Nour, 2013; Hodge, 2008). Once obtained, these individuals are then forced into prostitution or other forms of commercial sexual exploitation such as child pornography or work in strip clubs, massage parlors, or escort services.

Sexual exploitation is often associated with significant deprivation and with physical and psychological abuse. For those entrenched in the trafficking industry, it is very difficult to escape. Sex trafficking is associated with significant psychological and physical health consequences, including sexually transmitted infections, HIV/AIDS, depression, and PTSD (Deshpande & Nour, 2013; Hodge, 2008). Risk factors associated with sex trafficking are multifaceted and include individual, structural, and economic factors such as poverty, gender bias, living in vulnerable areas, and demand for commercial sex and economic profits (Deshpande & Nour, 2013; Hodge, 2008).

Combat-Related Trauma

Combat trauma refers to direct or indirect exposures to extremely stressful events in a war zone and includes situations such as experiencing serious injuries, witnessing the serious injury or death of a friend, exposure to hostile enemy or friendly fire, and exposure to rocket attacks, bombs, and the grotesque (e.g., seeing and smelling decomposing dead bodies). In combat situations, the threat of danger and death is often constant, placing service members on a constant state of alert. Service members may also have to wound or kill enemy combatants or civilians while on duty and are often witness to brutality toward detainees. Being away from home for extended periods of time adds a further layer of stress.

Recent military actions (OEF and OIF) are unique in that a higher proportion of service members are being deployed for longer and multiple periods of time with limited breaks in between (Tanielian, 2009). Moreover, with the advent of new safety technology, more OEF/OIF service members are surviving their injuries and avoiding death than in the Vietnam and Korean wars. Although a significant proportion of veterans do not develop PTSD, the extent and severity of their psychological distress depends on pre-, peri-, and postdeployment factors such as history of childhood trauma, intensity and duration of combat exposure, and military, family, social, and political support on return home (Richardson, Frueh, & Acierno, 2010).

Civilian War Trauma and Torture

Civilian exposure to armed conflicts, war traumas, and torture is quite common and occurs on a large scale across the world. During the last 60 years, there have been a documented 200 civil conflicts or wars during which serious human rights violations have occurred (Johnson & Thompson, 2008; Kienzler, 2008). Civilians exposed to war are often exposed to multiple cumulative traumas, including torture, defined as any psychological or physical act that intentionally inflicts severe pain or suffering in service of obtaining information, confession, or punishment for a perceived transgression (United Nations General Assembly, 1984).

Steel et al. (2009) conducted a systematic review and meta-analysis of studies related to torture and found that 21% of participants in 84 surveys reported personal experiences of torture. In addition to the direct experiences of war, such as exposure to physical assault, brutal killings, massacres, torture, destruction of personal property, and loss or disappearance of loved ones, populations exposed to war traumas also have to face additional stressors such as displacement to refugee camps, loss of social networks, and exposure to extreme poverty and poor living conditions, all of which compound the already profound psychological and physical effects of war trauma (Miller & Rasmussen, 2010).

In 2012, the United Nations High Commissioner for Refugees estimated that there were 15.4 million forcibly displaced refugees worldwide, 28.8 million internally displaced people, and 893,700 asylum seekers, highlighting the large numbers of people affected by war trauma and possibly in need of mental health services (United Nations Refugee Agency, 2013). Studies indicate that greater exposure to cumulative war traumas, female gender, age (children and the elderly), and refugee status were significant risk factors for the development of subsequent PTSD or other psychiatric distress (Murthy & Lakshminarayana, 2006). In contrast, social support, level of preparedness for torture, and certain belief systems were protective factors in the aftermath of war (Johnson & Thompson, 2008).

Disasters

Disasters are large-scale traumatic events, often called "mass traumas," that are experienced collectively by many groups of people who may suffer from direct or indirect experiences, such as physical harm, loss of a loved one, destruction of personal and community property, depletion of social resources, and identification with those worst affected. The spectrum of consequences associated with disasters is vast and includes personal, communal, and economic aspects. Moreover, the psychological consequences in the aftermath of disasters are variable and depend on a combination of individual characteristics, extent and severity of disaster exposure, and level of postdisaster social resources (Arnberg, Johannesson, & Michel, 2013; Neria, Nandi, & Galea, 2008; Norris, 2006). Since disasters are unpredictable in their occurrence, it is often difficult for researchers to quickly enter the field to assess the immediate consequences and longitudinal course of recovery (Neria et al., 2008; Norris, 2006).

Disasters are often categorized in several ways: (1) *man-made disasters*, such as the September 11, 2001, terrorist attacks on New York City and Washington, DC, or the 1995 Oklahoma City bombing, (2) *technological disasters*, such as the 1989 Exxon Valdez oil spill in Alaska or the 2001 Chernobyl nuclear power plant accident in Ukraine, and (3) *natural disasters*, such as the 2004 tsunami in Asia and the 2005 Hurricane Katrina in the United States. Disasters are further classified in terms of scale, from those that affect hundreds of people to those that might affect an entire nation, and in terms of outcome (i.e., the psychological and physical effect on those directly and indirectly affected; Neria et al., 2008).

Neria et al. (2008) conducted a systematic review of posttraumatic stress subsequent to disasters and found that among those who experienced man-made disasters, PTSD was most prevalent among survivors (those directly exposed to the event) and first responders or rescue workers. Technological disasters also had a high rate of PTSD prevalence among survivors and rescue workers (15%–75%). Exposure to natural disasters led to lower rates of PTSD prevalence compared to man-made and technological disasters (Neria et al., 2008). Neria and colleagues point out, however, that studies of natural disasters tend to combine those directly and indirectly affected, which may dilute the average level of severity of exposure to the disaster and resultant PTSD.

Longitudinal studies—research in which people are studied at regular intervals over the course of many years—on man-made and technological disasters indicate a general decline in PTSD prevalence over time (Neria et al., 2008). However, as noted by Arnberg et al. (2013), longitudinal studies often do not cover enough years to provide reliable estimates of the course of PTSD. Another difficulty associated with obtaining proper estimates of the psychological distress experienced in the aftermath of disaster is determining who exactly are the disaster victims. As expected, studies show that those most directly affected had the highest rates of psychiatric distress and the general population the least. But what about those who may have been traumatized by the media coverage of a disaster? Because of the scope of disasters, especially natural disasters, it can be difficult to assess all those affected. Also, cross-cultural differences in disaster readiness, wealth distribution, and what theorists call "collateral stressors," or secondary stressors, all contribute to the negative consequences that disasters may leave behind (Arnberg et al., 2013).

Serious Accidents

Motor vehicle accidents (MVAs) are one of the most common causes of traumatic stress. In 2011, close to 1.5 million individuals were injured in MVAs (National Highway Traffic Safety Administration, 2013). Males are more likely to report exposure to MVAs than women (35% versus 15%, respectively; Buckley, 2013). Often these accidents lead to significant chronic pain, disability, or even death. Significant predictors of psychological distress post-MVA include the amount of physical injury experienced, rate of recovery from the accident, and level of social support (Buckley, 2013).

Life-Threatening Medical Illness

Being diagnosed with a life-threatening medical illness such as breast cancer or lung cancer or learning that a family member has a life-threatening illness can also be another source of traumatic stress. A recent study found that 23% of 1,139 women who were newly diagnosed with breast cancer reported symptoms of PTSD (Vin-Raviv et al., 2013). Black and Asian women were more likely to develop PTSD symptoms in response to their cancer diagnosis than White females. The experience of receiving the diagnosis, obtaining treatment for one's illness, worrying about side effects of the treatments, and fearing recurrence of the illness may all contribute to the development of significant psychological distress.

OUR GOALS FOR THIS BOOK

The preceding review shows the wide range of events that can cause psychological trauma. But there is much more to know about this field. Research on trauma over the past 3 decades has been rich and varied. Our goal in this book is to provide an overview of these findings. For example, there is a strong evidence base that describes the effects of trauma on both physical and mental well-being. Researchers have also identified the types of treatment that are the most likely to be effective. We now understand much of the mechanism by which trauma can affect mental and physical health, as well as how clinicians can help their clients avoid these problems. Researchers have found that family members of people with PTSD also suffer, and organizations such as the National Center for PTSD offer specific suggestions to help families cope. And we now know that trauma survivors can also experience posttraumatic growth. These are perhaps the most hopeful findings in this field.

We hope that you find this topic as interesting as we do. There is always room for more workers in this field, or for more people who are trauma-aware. It's an exciting time to be in this field.

REFERENCES

American Psychiatric Association. (1980). *Diagnostic and statistical manual of mental disorders* (3rd ed.). Washington, DC: Author.

American Psychiatric Association. (2000). *Diagnostic and statistical manual of mental disorders* (4th ed., text revision). Washington, DC: Author.

American Psychiatric Association. (2013). *Diagnostic and statistical manual of mental disorders* (5th ed.). Washington, DC: Author.

Arnberg, F. K., Johannesson, K. B., & Michel, P. O. (2013). Prevalence and duration of PTSD in survivors six years after a natural disaster. *Journal of Anxiety Disorders, 27*(3), 347–352.

Bent-Goodley, T. B. (2007). Health disparities and violence against women: Why and how cultural and societal influences matter. *Trauma, Violence, & Abuse, 8*(2), 90–104.

Black, M. C., Basile, K. C., Breiding, M. J., Smith, S. G., Walters, M. L., Merrick, M. T., & Stevens, M. R. (2011). *The National Intimate Partner and Sexual Violence Survey (NISVS): 2010 summary report.* Atlanta, GA: National Center for Injury Prevention and Control, Centers for Disease Control and Prevention.

Breiding, M. J., Black, M. C., & Ryan, G. W. (2008). Prevalence and risk factors of intimate partner violence in eighteen U.S. states/territories, 2005. *American Journal of Preventive Medicine, 34*(2), 112–118. 10.1016/j.amepre.2007.10.001

Breslau, N. (2009). The epidemiology of trauma, PTSD, and other post-trauma disorders. *Trauma, Violence, & Abuse, 10*(3), 198–210. doi: 10.1177/1524838009334448

Briere, J., & Scott, C. (2012). *Principles of trauma therapy* (2nd ed.). New York, NY: Sage.

Buckley, T. (2013). *Traumatic stress and motor vehicle accidents.* Retrieved November 24, 2013, from http://www.ptsd.va.gov/professional/pages/traumatic-stress-vehicle-accidents.asp

Centers for Disease Control and Prevention (CDC). (2013, April). *Understanding intimate partner violence.* Retrieved November 24, 2013, from http://www.cdc.gov/VIOLENCEPREVENTION/intimate partnerviolence

Child Abuse Prevention and Treatment Act (CAPTA), The CAPTA Reauthorization Act of 2010, Public Law 111–320 (42 U.S.C. 5106a). Retrieved November 24, 2013, from http://www.gpo.gov/fdsys/pkg/BILLS-111s3817enr/pdf

Cicchetti, D., & Toth, S. L. (2005). Child maltreatment. *Annual Review of Clinical Psychology, 1,* 409–438. doi:10.1146/annurev.clinpsy.1.102803.144029

Crosson-Towers, C. (2009). *Understanding child abuse and neglect* (8th ed.). Upper Saddle River, NJ: Pearson.

Deshpande, N. A., & Nour, N. M. (2013). Sex trafficking of women and girls. *Reviews in Obstetrics and Gynecology, 6*(1), e22–e27.

Ehrensaft, M. K., Moffitt, T. E., & Caspi, A. (2004). Clinically abusive relationships in an unselected birth cohort: Men's and women's participation and developmental antecedents. *Journal of Abnormal Psychology, 113*(2), 258. doi:10.1037/0021-843X.113.2.258

Field, C. A., & Caetano, R. (2004). Ethnic differences in intimate partner violence in the U.S. general population: The role of alcohol use and socioeconomic status. *Trauma, Violence, & Abuse, 5*(4), 303–317.

Field, C. A., & Caetano, R. (2005). Intimate partner violence in the U.S. general population: Progress and future directions. *Journal of Interpersonal Violence, 20*(4), 463–469.

Finkel, E. J., & Eckhardt, C. I. (2011). Intimate partner violence. In *The Oxford handbook of close relationships.* New York, NY: Oxford.

Hampton, R., Oliver, W., & Magarian, L. (2003). Domestic violence in the African American community: An analysis of social and structural factors. *Violence Against Women, 9*(5), 533–557. doi:10.1177/1077801202250450

Hampton, R. L., & Gelles, R. J. (1994). Violence toward Black women in a nationally representative sample of Black families. *Journal of Comparative Family Studies, 25*(1), 105–119.

Heim, C., Shugart, M., Craighead, W. E., & Nemeroff, C. B. (2010). Neurobiological and psychiatric consequences of child abuse and neglect. *Developmental Psychobiology, 52*(7), 671–690. doi:10.1002/dev.20494

Hien, D., & Ruglass, L. (2009). Interpersonal partner violence and women in the United States: An overview of prevalence rates, psychiatric correlates and consequences and barriers to help seeking. *International Journal of Law and Psychiatry, 32*(1), 48. doi:10.1016/j.ijlp.2008.11.003

Hodge, D. R. (2008). Sexual trafficking in the United States: A domestic problem with transnational dimensions. *Social Work, 53*(2), 143–152. doi:10.1093/sw/53.2.143

Johnson, H., & Thompson, A. (2008). The development and maintenance of post-traumatic stress disorder (PTSD) in civilian adult survivors of war trauma and torture: A review. *Clinical Psychology Review, 28*(1), 36–47.

Jordan, C. E. (2004). Intimate partner violence and the justice system: An examination of the interface. *Journal of Interpersonal Violence, 19*(12), 1412–1434. doi:10.1177/0886260504269697

Jordan, C. E., Campbell, R., & Follingstad, D. (2010). Violence and women's mental health: The impact of physical, sexual, and psychological aggression. *Annual Review of Clinical Psychology, 6*(1), 607–628.

Kessler, R. C., Chiu, W. T., Demler, O., & Walters, E. E. (2005). Prevalence, severity, and comorbidity of 12-month *DSM-IV* disorders in the National Comorbidity Survey Replication. *Archives of General Psychiatry, 62*(6), 617.

Kienzler, H. (2008). Debating war-trauma and post-traumatic stress disorder (PTSD) in an interdisciplinary arena. *Social Science & Medicine, 67*(2), 218–227.

Kimerling, R., Street, A. E., Pavao, J., Smith, M. W., Cronkite, R. C., Holmes, T. H., & Frayne, S. M. (2010). Military-related sexual trauma among Veterans Health Administration patients returning from Afghanistan and Iraq. *American Journal of Public Health, 100*(8), 1409–1412.

Mennen, F. E., Kim, K., Sang, J., & Trickett, P. K. (2010). Child neglect: Definition and identification of youth's experiences in official reports of maltreatment. *Child Abuse and Neglect, 34*(9), 647–658. doi:10.1016/j.chiabu.2010.02.007

Miller, K. E., & Rasmussen, A. (2010). War exposure, daily stressors, and mental health in conflict and post-conflict settings: Bridging the divide between trauma-focused and psychosocial frameworks. *Social Science & Medicine, 70*(1), 7–16.

Muela, A., de Arana, E. L., Barandiaran, A., Larrea, I., & Vitoria, J. R. (2012). Definition, incidence and psychopathological consequences of child abuse and neglect. In A. Muela (Ed.), *Child abuse and neglect: A multidimensional approach* (pp. 1–20). Rijeka, Croatia: InTech.

Murthy, R. S., & Lakshminarayana, R. (2006). Mental health consequences of war: A brief review of research findings. *World Psychiatry, 5*(1), 25–30.

National Highway Traffic Safety Administration. (2013). *Traffic Safety Facts 2011.* Retrieved from http://www.nrd.nhtsa.dot.gov/Pubs/811754AR.PDF

Neria, Y., Nandi, A., & Galea, S. (2008). Post-traumatic stress disorder following disasters: A systematic review. *Psychological Medicine, 38*(4), 467–480.

Norris, F. (2006). Disaster research methods: Past progress and future directions. *Journal of Traumatic Stress, 19*(2), 173–184. doi:10.1002/jts.20109

Pereda, N., Guilera, G., Forns, M., & Gómez-Benito, J. (2009). The prevalence of child sexual abuse in community and student samples: A meta-analysis. *Clinical Psychology Review, 29*(4), 328–338. doi:10.1016/j.cpr.2009.02.007

Rennison, C. M., & Welchans, S. (2000, May). *Intimate partner violence,* NCJ No. 178247. Washington, DC: U.S. Department of Justice.

Richardson, L. K., Frueh, B. C., & Acierno, R. (2010). Prevalence estimates of combat-related post-traumatic stress disorder: Critical review. *Australian and New Zealand Journal of Psychiatry, 44*(1), 4–19. doi:10.3109/00048670903393597

Rowe, E. L., Gradus, J. L., Pineles, S. L., Batten, S. V., & Davison, E. H. (2009). Military sexual trauma in treatment-seeking women veterans. *Military Psychology, 21*(3), 387–395. doi:10.1080/08995600902914768

Sorenson, S. B., Upchurch, D. M., & Shen, H. (1996). Violence and injury in marital arguments: Risk patterns and gender differences. *American Journal of Public Health, 86*, 35–40.

Steel, Z., Chey, T., Silove, D., Marnane, C., Bryant, R. A., & Van Ommeren, M. (2009). Association of torture and other potentially traumatic events with mental health outcomes among populations exposed to mass conflict and displacement: A systematic review and meta-analysis. *JAMA, 302*(5), 537–549.

Suris, A., & Lind, L. (2008). Military sexual trauma: A review of prevalence and associated health consequences in veterans. *Trauma, Violence, & Abuse, 9,* 250–269.

Tanielian, T. (2009). *Assessing combat exposure and post-traumatic stress disorder in troops and estimating the costs to society: Implications from the RAND Invisible Wounds of War Study.* Retrieved from http://www.rand.org/pubs/testimonies/CT321.html

Tjaden, P., & Thoennes, N. (2000). Prevalence and consequences of male-to-female and female-to-male intimate partner violence as measured by the National Violence Against Women Survey. *Violence Against Women, 6,* 142–161.

United Nations General Assembly. (1984, December 10). Convention Against Torture and Other Cruel, Inhuman or Degrading Treatment or Punishment. *United Nations Treaty Series,* Vol. 1465, p. 85.

United Nations Refugee Agency. (2013). *Facts and figures about refugees.* Retrieved November 25, 2013, from http://www.unhcr.org.uk/about-us/key-facts-and-figures.html

U.S. Department of Health and Human Services' Children's Bureau (2011). *Child Maltreatment Report, 2011.* Washington, DC: Author. Retrieved from www.acf.hhs.gov/sites/default/files/cb/cm11.pdf

U.S. Department of Veterans Affairs. (2014). *Military sexual trauma.* Retrieved from http://www.mentalhealth.va.gov/docs/mst_general_factsheet.pdf

U.S. State Department. (2013). *Trafficking in Persons Report, 2013.* Retrieved from http://www.state.gov/documents/organization/210737.pdf

Victims of Trafficking and Violence Protection Act of 2000 [United States of America], Public Law 106-386 [H.R. 3244], 28 October 2000.

Vin-Raviv, N., Hillyer, G. C., Hershman, D. L., Galea, S., Leoce, N., Bovbjerg, D. H., . . . Neugut, A. I. (2013). Racial disparities in post-traumatic stress after diagnosis of localized breast cancer: The BQUAL study. *Journal of the National Cancer Institute, 105*(8), 563–572.

Walton-Moss, B. J., Manganello, J., Frye, V., & Campbell, J. C. (2005). Risk factors for intimate partner violence and associated injury among urban women. *Journal of Community Health, 30*(5), 377–389.

West, C. M. (2004). Black women and intimate partner violence: New directions for research. *Journal of Interpersonal Violence, 19,* 1487–1493.

How Do You Diagnose Posttraumatic Stress Disorder?

A BRIEF HISTORY OF THE POSTTRAUMATIC STRESS DISORDER (PTSD) DIAGNOSIS

hroughout the 1970s and 1980s, several social movements called attention to the psychological reactions of people exposed to stressful events and called for a mental health diagnostic category that more adequately captured the emotional reactions of these individuals. Advocacy groups drew increased attention to military veterans who demonstrated enduring psychological complications after exposure to war traumas and chronic difficulties in readjusting to civilian living (Friedman, Resick, & Keane, 2007). These were times during which traumatic stress reactions in the military were categorized under terms such as *shell shock, combat exhaustion,* and *gross stress reactions.*

While denouncing rape, domestic violence, and child abuse, the women's movement during this time drew convincing correlations between the responses of civilian victims of trauma and American survivors of military combat (Friedman et al., 2007). The contributions of these social movements, and the increased evidence of an epidemic of insufficiently addressed trauma, moved the U.S. government to establish federal laws that now mandate the report of suspected child abuse or neglect and that now are used to prosecute domestic violence offenders (Friedman et al., 2007). In addition to changes in laws to protect victims, there was an increase in social support and services for women and children that had been abused.

These contributions also motivated the American Psychiatric Association (APA) to include posttraumatic stress disorder (PTSD) for the first time in the third edition of its classification system, the *Diagnostic and Statistical Manual of Mental Disorders* (*DSM-III;* APA, 1980). A relatively new and controversial psychiatric diagnostic category, PTSD is the only psychiatric disorder in the *DSM* that requires exposure to a traumatic event (criterion A stressor, defined hereafter) to meet the diagnosis.

In the *DSM-III,* a traumatic event was defined as "a recognizable stressor that would evoke significant symptoms of distress in almost anyone" (APA, 1980, p. 236). However, many clinicians found the definition to be too brief and vague (Friedman et al., 2007; Weathers & Keane, 2007). In 1987, the *DSM-III-R* redefined a traumatic event as "an event that is outside the range of usual human experience that would be markedly distressing to almost anyone." This definition also drew criticism, because exposure to traumatic events is far from rare. Some people experience traumatic episodes on a regular basis (Weathers & Keane, 2007). Moreover, the *DSM-III-R* provided little reliable guidance to help clinicians discern which events were "outside the range of usual human experience." Despite limitations pertaining to defining the parameters of trauma, this newly established diagnosis of PTSD ushered in a wealth of research on the prevalence and consequences of trauma exposure, furthering the development of assessment measures, psychological treatment approaches, and the pharmacological treatment of PTSD.

With each subsequent revision of the *DSM* (e.g., the *DSM-IV* [APA, 1994] and the *DSM-IV Text Revision* [*DSM-IV-TR*; APA, 2000]), alterations were made to the diagnostic criteria for PTSD. Changes centered on that which objectively constitutes a *traumatic stressor*, clarifying the nature of emotional responses to traumatic events, and the behavioral symptoms that might occur in response to trauma exposure.

According to the *DSM-IV-TR*, a person could be diagnosed with PTSD only if he or she experienced a criterion A stressor, which comprises two components: (1) The person experienced, witnessed, or was confronted with an event or events that involved actual threatened death or serious injury, or a threat to the physical integrity of self or others, and (2) the person's response involved intense fear, helplessness, or horror (in children, this may be expressed instead by disorganized or agitated behavior). Furthermore, the person had to also report several additional psychological symptoms that are part of the three PTSD symptom clusters. The PTSD symptom clusters include (1) re-experiencing symptoms, such as intrusive thoughts, nightmares, and flashbacks about the traumatic event (criterion B), (2) avoidance of trauma-related stimuli, such as memories, thoughts, feelings, or places associated with the trauma (criterion C), emotional numbing (i.e., the inability to experience positive feelings, criterion C), and (3) hyperarousal symptoms, including difficulty falling or staying asleep, irritability or anger, and increased startle response (criterion D). These symptoms had to cause significant distress and impairment lasting at least 1 month. Both the *DSM-IV* and *DSM-IV-TR* provide specific examples of events that could potentially qualify as traumatic events.

Despite these changes, significant criticisms continued against the *DSM-IV*'s criteria for PTSD diagnosis. For some, the definition of a traumatic event seemed too broad, primed to lead to an increase in the prevalence rate of people exposed to traumatic events and thus potentially overdiagnosis of PTSD

(Breslau & Kessler, 2001; Friedman et al., 2007; Kilpatrick, Resnick, & Acierno, 2009; McNally, 2003; Weathers & Keane, 2007). Others expressed concern that the PTSD diagnosis would pathologize normal reactions to traumatic events (Brewin et al., 2009; Kilpatrick et al., 2009; McNally, 2003; Spitzer et al., 2007; Weathers & Keane, 2007). Still others argued that PTSD is a culture-bound syndrome that does not adequately capture the emotional experiences of people outside the Western Hemisphere (Friedman et al., 2007).

Friedman, Keane, and Resick (2007) cogently addressed these and other criticisms of PTSD in their seminal handbook on PTSD. They noted that most individuals recover from traumatic events—resilience is the norm (Bonnano, 2004). Yet there is a subgroup of individuals who develop PTSD and who may require treatment. The diagnosis is an informative tool for treatment planning. While there are culturally bound expressions of distress, evidence suggests that PTSD is a universally relevant diagnosis. PTSD has been documented as a traumatic stress response across the world (De Jong, Komproe, & Van Ommeren, 2003).

After 14 years of revisions, the APA recently released the *DSM-5* (APA, 2013), with significant revisions to the diagnostic criteria for PTSD. PTSD now belongs to a new diagnostic category of trauma and stressor-related disorders instead of the former category of anxiety disorders. The *DSM-5* provides a clearer delineation of what constitutes traumatic events and reconceptualizes the number and types of PTSD symptom clusters that a person might experience after exposure to a traumatic event. The *DSM-5* identifies an event as traumatic if a person has experienced "exposure to actual or threatened death, serious injury, or sexual violence" (APA, 2013, p. 271). The individual's subjective responses of intense fear, helplessness, or horror are no longer diagnostic requirements (as they were in the *DSM-IV*). This omission is based on research findings that indicate that an individual's subjective responses to trauma are not reliably predictive of the subsequent development of PTSD (APA, 2013). In the *DSM-5*, PTSD symptom clusters have now been expanded from three to four.

Symptoms clusters now include (1) intrusion or re-experiencing symptoms (criterion B), (2) avoidance symptoms (criterion C), (3) negative alterations in cognitions and mood (criterion D), and (4) alterations in arousal and reactivity (criterion E).

Criterion D (negative alterations in cognitions and mood) is a new PTSD diagnostic criterion that includes symptoms such as dissociative amnesia (i.e., memory loss for important aspects of the traumatic event), persistent and irrational beliefs about oneself and the world (e.g., "the world is unsafe," "people cannot be trusted"), persistent and irrational beliefs about why the traumatic event occurred (e.g., "the traumatic event was my fault"), persistent negative emotions (e.g., shame, guilt, fear), difficulty experiencing positive emotions (i.e., emotional numbing), feelings of detachment/estrangement from people, and loss of interest in activities that used to be enjoyable. Criterion E (alterations in arousal and reactivity) now incorporates symptoms such as irritable and aggressive behaviors toward others, self-destructive behaviors such as reckless driving or substance abuse, increased scanning of one's environment for signs of threat, heightened startle reactions, and problems with concentration and sleep. As before, the symptoms must last 1 month and cause significant psychological distress or functional impairment.

The *DSM-5* revision of the PTSD diagnosis now allows for the specification of a dissociative subtype of PTSD. Dissociation refers to a psychological process wherein the mind disconnects or separates bodily experiences, thoughts, feelings, and memories (see Chapter 9 for further information; Colangelo, 2009). Individuals who meet the PTSD diagnostic criteria and have additional symptoms of dissociation, such as depersonalization (i.e., the experience of feeling disconnected or detached from one's body) or derealization (i.e., the experience of feeling that one's external environment is unreal or hazy), would qualify for this specification. Moreover, for those individuals whose symptoms do not meet full diagnostic criteria until at least 6 months after trauma exposure, a specification of "with delayed expression" is allowable.

Finally, the *DSM-5* provides new and separate PTSD diagnostic criteria for children 6 years and younger. Neglected in previous editions of the *DSM*, PTSD in very young children was an understudied and misunderstood phenomenon. This new diagnostic criteria set now enhances the proper diagnosis and treatment of PTSD in young children.

PTSD ASSESSMENT

Clients may be assessed for PTSD during an interview with a psychiatrist, psychologist, or other licensed mental health clinician. The assessment of trauma exposure and PTSD is a challenging and multidimensional process. The establishment of a collaborative therapeutic alliance with the client is essential to the fulfillment of assessment objectives. The clinician asks candid questions about traumatic stressors which the client may be reluctant to discuss. Sensitivity and empathy are crucial to establishing a therapeutic alliance.

Obstacles to Disclosure

Many clients have not shared their trauma histories with anyone before the assessment. Memories of trust violations may make it difficult for clients to disclose. Obstacles to disclosure may also include worries about confidentiality, shame, or guilt about having participated in the traumatic experience and fear of negative responses from the interviewer or clinician (Briere & Scott, 2012). Clients are often keenly attuned to verbal and nonverbal reactions to their stories. Clients with trauma histories may anticipate responses of blame and disbelief. It is thus important for the clinician to give focused attention to the client's responses throughout the interview while instilling an ambience of safety, support, and trust. The clinician will need to utilize appropriate listening skills and empathy to convey sincere interest in learning about the client's past experiences.

Goals of Assessment

A key component of conducting a PTSD assessment is the consideration of the goals of the assessment, since they will influence the types of methods utilized to conduct the evaluation. Objectives may include obtaining a differential diagnosis and a treatment plan in a clinical setting, identifying psychological issues that may serve as mitigating factors in a forensic or legal context, and determining whether a person meets the inclusion criteria for participation in research. Depending on the objectives, one can select measures most appropriate for the assessment situation.

To ensure the validity of the diagnosis, information must be obtained from multiple measures and multiple sources. In addition to the clinical interview, the clinician may need to gather collateral information from the client's family members and friends and from clinical records. Empirically validated self-report measures and psychological tests (as well as available psychophysiological measures) are also recommended to increase the validity of the PTSD diagnosis. Before conducting the evaluation, it is appropriate for the clinician to inform the client of the purpose and value of the evaluation, as well as any limits to confidentiality that may surround the information gathered (Briere & Scott, 2012).

Hierarchical Order of the Assessment Process

Briere and Scott (2012) recommend a hierarchical order to the assessment process. First, the clinician needs to conduct a *safety and threat assessment* to ensure the client is not at risk of further traumatization and is not a danger to self or others. Second, the clinician needs to determine whether the client is *psychologically stable* enough to partake in the assessment. Depending on the recency of the traumatic event and the client's emotional state, he or she may not be able to tolerate the detailed inquiry involved in a trauma assessment. Care must be taken to ascertain whether the client is emotionally stable and capable of participating in the assessment process and to ensure that the experience does not unnecessarily trigger a traumatic response. Keen attention to the emotions and behaviors that can occur in response to the assessment process (e.g., overwhelming emotions, avoidance of certain topics, and dissociation), as well as offering support-ive interventions when appropriate, is strongly recommended (Briere & Scott, 2012).

American Psychological Association's Division of Trauma Psychology Assessment Guidelines

The American Psychological Association's Division of Trauma Psychology recently developed a set of guidelines regarding the assessment of trauma in adults (Unpublished manuscript, 2012). Key recommendations include the following:

1. Gain familiarity with the wide range of reactions to trauma exposure (i.e., PTSD is only one of the many possible reac-tions that a person might display; others may be short-lived and remit over time).
2. Remember that trauma assessments cannot determine whether an event *actually* occurred. Trauma assessments can only indicate whether or not the client's responses are consis-tent with those typical of reactions to trauma exposure.

Key tasks in establishing a PTSD diagnosis include (1) determining whether or not the client has been exposed to a criterion A traumatic event, (2) determining the presence, frequency, and severity of the individual symptoms of PTSD, (3) establishing whether there is a connection between the symptoms reported and the traumatic event experienced, (4) determining whether the client's symptoms cause emotional distress or impairment in relationships and in educational or employment endeavors, (5) establishing whether the symptom duration criterion of 1 month has been met, and (6) specifying whether the PTSD diagnosis meets criteria for a dissociative subtype or whether the symptoms were of delayed onset and expression (APA, 2013).

Depending on the goal of the assessment, a determination of the individual's response style will be crucial in determining whether the client is fabricating his or her symptoms or has secondary motives for appearing worse off than he or she might actually be (Lange, Sullivan, & Scott, 2010).

CHALLENGES TO THE DIFFERENTIAL DIAGNOSIS OF PTSD

In addition to challenges associated with a client's willingness to disclose his or her experiences, there are challenges related to the differential diagnosis of PTSD with co-occurring psychiatric disorders that may complicate the diagnostic picture. Studies indicate that individuals with PTSD typically have one or more other psychiatric diagnoses (Schillaci et al., 2009). Since several of the PTSD symptoms overlap with other psychiatric disorders (e.g., depression and anxiety disorders), care must be taken when assigning symptoms to a particular diagnostic category.

More generally, PTSD needs to be differentiated from an acute stress disorder (ASD) or an adjustment disorder. The client has to have been exposed to an *extreme* stressor (e.g., there was real or threatened death, injury, or sexual violence). In contrast, in adjustment disorder, the severity of the stressor can be of any kind. PTSD and acute stress disorder (ASD) are distinguished by the duration and the nature of the psychological symptoms following exposure to a traumatic event. In ASD, trauma reactions and symptoms occur and resolve within 3 days to 4 weeks after exposure to a traumatic event (APA, 2013;

Bryant, Friedman, Spiegel, Ursano, & Strain, 2011). In contrast, a diagnosis of PTSD cannot be assigned unless the individual has experienced symptoms for at least 4 weeks.

Complex PTSD

In contrast to those who have experienced a single traumatic event, individuals who have been exposed to early onset, prolonged, and severe traumatic experiences (e.g., chronic child abuse or neglect, long-term domestic violence, torture, or war imprisonment) may present with psychiatric difficulties that may be inadequately captured by the PTSD diagnosis. Complex PTSD (Cloitre et al., 2011; Herman, 1992; Resick et al., 2012) and disorders of extreme stress not otherwise specified (DESNOS; Pelcovitz et al., 1997) are two categories used to capture psychiatric syndromes that may occur in response to prolonged and severe traumas. These psychological disturbances are typically described as difficulties in self-regulatory capacities and are categorized into five domains: (1) emotion regulation problems, (2) disturbances in relational capacities, (3) alterations in attention and concentration (e.g. dissociation), (4) somatic distress or disorganization, and (5) alterations in belief systems (Cloitre et al., 2011; Resick et al., 2012).

In the *DSM-IV-TR*, several of these symptom domains were listed as associated features of PTSD (Cloitre et al., 2011). The dearth of research on these constructs has rendered inconclusive results regarding their validity. Neither complex PTSD nor DESNOS is formally recognized as a separate diagnostic category in the *DSM-IV* and the *DSM-5*. Nevertheless, the identification and description of these core symptom domains have brought significant attention to the differences in adaptations that can occur after exposure to different types and severity of trauma, and they allow for the development and testing of assessment measures and treatment approaches that effectively treat these disturbances (Cloitre et al., 2011; Resick et al., 2012).

ASSESSMENT METHODS

When considering the selection of specific tests or measures for the assessment of PTSD, there are several related constructs to consider, including reliability and validity.

Reliability refers to the degree to which a measure provides similar results across repeated administrations. There are several types of reliability that one can examine before selecting a test. *Test–retest reliability* refers to the consistency of the measure over time when administered to the same person or sample on two separate occasions. Test–retest reliability measures the extent to which observations on each of those occasions are correlated. *Interrater reliability* refers to the degree to which two different raters or judges agree on an observation—for example, the extent to which two evaluators, utilizing the same assessment instrument, agree on a diagnosis of PTSD.

Internal consistency measures the degree to which scores on different items on the test that measure similar underlying constructs are associated with each other. For example, if a PTSD self-report measure has 12 different items measuring PTSD and has high internal consistency, that means the responses to the 12 items are highly correlated with each other. If a measure has high internal consistency, that means the items are measuring similar things. Cronbach's alpha coefficient is an estimate of the internal consistency of a measure.

Validity refers to the extent to which the test measures what it is supposed to measure. In essence, this concept refers to the accuracy of the measure. A test must have high reliability in order to be valid. If a test has low reliability, then the validity of the construct would be called into question, because that indicates that the test has a lot of error or noise. For example, if two clinicians cannot agree on the symptoms that constitute a diagnosis of PTSD, then that calls into question the validity of the PTSD diagnosis.

The two most common validity constructs that are relevant to the selection of tests for PTSD assessment include construct validity and criterion validity. *Construct validity* refers generally to the extent to which the test accurately measures the underlying construct being assessed. For example, does a PTSD measure actually measure purported reactions to trauma? *Criterion validity* refers to the extent to which the measure is associated with or can predict a client's behavior on some external criterion.

There are two aspects of criterion validity: concurrent validity and predictive validity. *Concurrent validity* refers to the degree to which the test is associated with an established measure of the construct, both of which are administered at the same time (e.g., a new measure of PTSD is correlated with an established measure of PTSD). If there is a high correlation between the two measures, then the criterion validity of the new measure is said to be high. *Predictive validity* refers to the degree to which performance on a current test is predictive of future performance on another test. For example, scores on a self-report measure of PTSD are correlated with scores on another measure of PTSD administered several months later by a clinician.

Structured Diagnostic Interviews

In addition to an unstructured clinical interview, the use of reliable and valid structured diagnostic interviews can complement and inform clinical judgment about the nature of an individual's posttrauma responses. While many of the structured clinical interviews require extensive training and take time to administer, they are important components of a comprehensive trauma-informed assessment.

The Clinician-Administered PTSD Scale for *DSM-5*. The Clinician-Administered PTSD Scale for *DSM-5* (CAPS-5; Weathers et al., 2013a) is a 30-item structured clinical interview used to determine a diagnosis of PTSD. The CAPS was recently revised according to the new diagnostic criteria from *DSM-5*. The CAPS has four PTSD symptom cluster subscales: intrusion, avoidance, negative alterations in cognitions and mood associated with the traumatic event, and marked alteration in arousal and reactivity. The symptoms from these subscales map onto the 20 *DSM-5* PTSD symptoms.

In addition to establishing the presence of each symptom, the CAPS measures the severity of each symptom on a 5-point severity rating scale (0 = absent, 1 = mild/subthreshold, 2 = moderate/threshold, 3 = severe/markedly elevated, and 4 = extreme/incapacitating). Severity ratings are based on the frequency and intensity of the symptoms and the resultant impact of these symptoms on the client's social interactions and work performance. Once it has been established that a symptom is present, the symptom's functional relatedness to the index traumatic event must be established and assigned a rating of definite, probable, or unlikely. The overall severity ratings of the CAPS allow for both *categorical* (PTSD is present or absent) and *continuous* (level of severity of PTSD symptoms) measures of PTSD. The CAPS allows for the ratings of symptoms according to three time points: "past week," "past month," and "lifetime." The CAPS promotes standardized administration of the interview through the provision of prompt questions, rating principles, and guidelines. These features enhance the reliability and validity of the PTSD diagnosis across interviewers and types of trauma populations.

Prior to administering the CAPS, the clinician administers the revised Life Events Checklist for *DSM-5* (LEC-5; Weathers et al., 2013b), which was developed concurrently with the CAPS, to establish whether the client was ever exposed to a criterion A traumatic event. The LEC-5 assesses exposure to 16 potentially traumatic events (e.g., physical assault, sexual assault, life-threatening illness or injury) that might lead to PTSD, and one additional item that captures any other very stressful life event or experience not assessed by the first 16 items. Clients are asked if the events happened directly to them, if they witnessed it, if they learned about it happening to someone close to them, or if they were exposed to it as part of their job. The LEC-5 has demonstrated adequate effectiveness as a stand-alone assessment of traumatic exposure, particularly when evaluating the consistency of events that actually happened to a respondent (Weathers et al., 2013a).

After completion of the LEC-5, the clinician asks the client to select one index trauma or several closely related index traumas that serve as the basis of the PTSD inquiry. The clinician then determines whether or not these potentially traumatic events meet the *DSM-5* threshold for qualifying traumatic events. If the potentially traumatic events qualify for the *DSM-5* definition of traumatic events, the client is asked to keep the traumatic event(s) in mind as the CAPS is administered to determine the presence and severity of each PTSD symptom. The CAPS severity ratings are based on the client's reports, as well as the clinician's judgment about the validity of the client's reports and observations of the behaviors/emotions (e.g., emotional numbing, concentration problems) displayed by the client during the assessment.

A PTSD diagnosis is determined by first dichotomizing individual symptoms as "present" or "absent," then following the *DSM-5* diagnostic rule (e.g., one criterion B symptom, two criterion C symptoms, two criterion D symptoms, two criterion E symptoms, and so forth). A symptom is considered present only if the corresponding item severity score is rated 2 = *moderate/ threshold* or higher. PTSD symptom cluster severity scores are calculated by summing the severity scores obtained from each symptom contained within the cluster; a total severity score is obtained by summing the symptom cluster subscale scores. After determining the onset and duration of PTSD symptoms, the clinician rates the impact of PTSD symptoms on the client's social and occupational functioning.

The CAPS should only be administered by qualified mental health professionals or researchers with training in diagnostic interviewing and differential diagnosis. The total assessment time for the CAPS typically ranges from 45 to 60 minutes. The CAPS based on *DSM-IV* has demonstrated excellent reliability and validity (Weathers, Keane, & Davidson, 2001). The reliability and validity of the revised CAPS-5 are currently being tested.

The Structured Clinical Interview for DSM-IV. The Structured Clinical Interview for *DSM-IV* is a semi-structured interview utilized in the assessment of the major *DSM-IV* axis I diagnoses (SCID-I; First, Spitzer, Gibbon, & Williams, 2002). There are several versions of the SCID, designed to meet the needs of clinical researchers and practitioners and translated into multiple languages. The SCID was designed to be administered by trained mental health professionals. The interview is organized by diagnostic modules that consist of standardized questions and follow-up prompts that are utilized to elicit information related to the disorder being assessed. The SCID allows for the assessment of diagnoses during two periods: current (the diagnostic criteria were met within the past month) and lifetime (the diagnostic criteria were met anytime in the past). The SCID-I PTSD module can be administered as a part of a full diagnostic battery or separately.

Similar to the CAPS, the SCID-I PTSD module begins with an assessment of whether the client was ever exposed to traumatic events. Information on the dates and duration of exposures are gathered. Next the client is asked to focus on the traumatic event that affected him or her the most and is led through a series of questions designed to assess each of the 17 *DSM-IV* PTSD symptoms. Depending on the nature of the responses, symptoms are coded as absent, subthreshold, or threshold (present). Additional questions serve to determine symptom duration and whether symptoms cause clinically significant distress or functional impairment.

The duration of SCID administration ranges from 30 minutes to 120 minutes, contingent on the nature and severity of the client's presenting concerns. While the SCID is a useful assessment tool, it only provides a dichotomous assessment of whether or not PTSD or a PTSD symptom is present. The clinician's ability to determine the severity level of PTSD symptoms is limited since the frequency and intensity of PTSD symptoms are not assessed. Moreover, the SCID–PTSD module focuses on the "worst" traumatic experience. This requires the clinician to document the impact of additional traumas independent of the SCID. Hundreds of studies have demonstrated the reliability and validity of the SCID-I PTSD module (Lobbestael, Leurgans, & Arntz, 2011; Zanarini et al., 2000).

The PTSD Symptom Scale Interview. The PTSD Symptom Scale Interview (PSS-I; Foa, Riggs, Dancu, & Rothbaum, 1993) is another widely utilized PTSD interview module through which a trained interviewer assesses the 17 PTSD symptoms listed in the *DSM-IV*. In addition to a categorical diagnosis of PTSD, a severity rating of symptoms can also be obtained. The PSS-I allows for the assessment of symptoms that have occurred over two time spans: the past 2 weeks and the past 1 month.

The PSS-I requires the selection of an index trauma (i.e., the trauma that has caused the most difficulty for the client) and then the probing and quantification of PTSD symptoms. After endorsing a PTSD symptom, the interviewer asks the client, "How often has this been happening?" Each symptom is rated on a combined frequency/severity scale ranging from 0 ("not at all") to 3 ("five or more times per week"/"very much"). An overall severity score can be obtained by summing the scores of each PTSD symptom. A PTSD diagnosis is contingent upon meeting the diagnostic criteria of the *DSM-IV*. Significant strengths of the PSS-I are that it requires relatively little time to administer (approximately 15–25 minutes) and that laypersons can administer it as well (Keane, Brief, Pratt, & Miller, 2007). The PSS-I has excellent reliability and validity (Foa et al., 1993, 2005; Foa & Tolin, 2000).

Self-Report Measures

There are numerous reliable and valid self-report measures that can augment clinical interviews. These measures have from 17 to 100 items and may take as few as 5 minutes to 20 minutes to complete. Some of these measures require focus on a single traumatic event. Others allow for the assessment of multiple traumas. Symptom items correspond to either *DSM-III-R* or

DSM-IV-TR PTSD criteria. Self-report measures can be utilized to screen for PTSD, to assign a preliminary diagnosis of PTSD before a more extensive clinical evaluation is conducted, or to monitor responses to treatment over time.[1] The following is a select review of the most widely used PTSD self-report measures.

The PTSD Checklist. The PTSD Checklist (PLC; Weathers, Litz, Huska, & Keane, 1994) is one of the most widely used measures of PTSD symptomatology. It is a 17-item self-report measure that assesses the symptoms of PTSD according to *DSM-IV* criteria. There are three versions of the PCL: the Military Version (PCL-M), the Civilian Version (PCL-C), and the Specific Version (PCL-S). All versions are similar except for the index stressor. In the PCL-M, it asks the person to report symptoms related to "stressful military experiences"; in the PCL-C, to "stressful experiences"; and in the PCL-S, to an identified "stressful experience." Symptoms are rated on a scale of 1 ("not at all bothersome") to 5 ("extremely bothersome"). There are several scoring algorithms that allow for a PTSD symptom severity score (ranging from 17 to 85) a diagnosis of PTSD based on *DSM-IV* criteria, and specific cutoff scores.

The PCL has demonstrated good internal consistency and retest reliability among military trauma, civilian trauma, and non-clinical samples (Adkins et al., 2008; Keen et al., 2008; Ruggiero, Del Ben, Scotti, & Rabalais, 2003; Weathers et al., 1994) and has also demonstrated good convergent and discriminant validity (Keen et al., 2008; Ruggiero et al., 2003). A limitation of the PCL is the failure to ascertain whether the index trauma meets the *DSM-IV* traumatic event threshold criterion. Nor does it allow for assessment of whether the symptoms meet the threshold for clinical significance or duration of disturbance. McDonald and Calhoun (2010) conducted a comprehensive review of the diagnostic accuracy of the PCL and found that while the PCL demonstrated significant utility as a screening tool for PTSD, it was less robust as a diagnostic tool; thus, they caution against using the PCL as a diagnostic measure.

Posttraumatic Diagnostic Scale. The Posttraumatic Diagnostic Scale (PDS; Foa, Cashman, Jaycox, & Perry, 1997) is a 49-item, four-part self-report measure based on the PSS-I (Foa et al., 1993). It provides a traumatic events checklist. The PDS inquires about the nature of the most upsetting traumatic event that the individual endorses (i.e., the objective features of the event such as life threat and injury and the individual's emotional reaction during exposure). The PDS assesses the 17 PTSD symptoms in terms of frequency and severity from 0 ("not at all or only one time") to 3 ("five or more times a week"/"almost always"). The PDS also assesses functional impairment due to presenting symptoms. The PDS yields both a preliminary categorical diagnosis of PTSD and a total PTSD symptom severity ranging from 0 to 51.

The reliability and validity of the PDS have been demonstrated with high correlations with other self-report measures of PTSD and strong convergent validity with the CAPS and the SCID–PTSD module (Foa et al., 1993, 1997; Griffin et al., 2004; Powers, Gillihan, Rosenfield, Jerud, & Foa, 2012).

Trauma Symptom Inventory. The Trauma Symptom Inventory (TSI; Briere, Elliott, Harris, & Cotman, 1995) is a 100-item inventory that assesses symptoms of acute stress disorder, PTSD, and other posttrauma reactions. It is one of the most popular self-report measures of trauma symptoms (Elhai, Gray, Kashdan, & Franklin, 2005). It has 10 clinical scales and three validity scales. Five of the clinical scales measure symptoms of anxious arousal, depression, anger or irritability, intrusive experiences, and defensive avoidance, which map onto the *DSM-IV-TR* PTSD diagnostic criteria. The remaining five clinical scales capture other common posttrauma reactions: dissociation, sexual concerns, dysfunctional sexual behavior, tension reduction behaviors, and impaired self-reference. Individuals are asked to rate how often they have experienced a symptom in the past 6 months on a scale of 0 ("never") to 3 ("often"). The TSI does not link the symptoms to a predefined traumatic event. A computer scoring program is available that converts the raw scores into T scores (i.e., standardized scores) and provides norms for both genders and various ages. The TSI requires 20 minutes to 40 minutes to administer and score.

The PTSD diagnosis is a common factor in the consideration of legal matters. In forensics, a PTSD diagnosis is considered in determining the sentence of the indicted. In other legal settings, a PTSD diagnosis is considered a relevant factor in the evaluation of personal injury or disability claims, situations in which the secondary gains of having a diagnosis of PTSD are high. There is a heightened need for validity scales that can help determine whether an individual is over- or underreporting his or her symptomatology (Resnick, West, & Payne, 2008). A strength of the TSI is the inclusion of three validity scales designed to detect responses that suggest atypical or inconsistent responding.

Overall, the TSI has demonstrated good internal consistency and concurrent validity with other acceptable measures of PTSD, including the CAPS (Briere, 1996). Its diagnostic utility has been demonstrated by its ability to differentiate between individuals with and without PTSD (Arbisi, Ben-Porath, & McNulty, 2006; McDevitt-Murphy, Weathers, Flood, Eakin, & Benson, 2007). However, in response to more recent concerns that the validity scales of the TSI were ineffective in establishing whether a person's responses were invalid (Arbisi et al., 2006), a second edition of the TSI (TSI-2; Briere, 2011) was developed with improved validity scales, new norms, and several new or configured clinical scales. The reliability and validity of the TSI-2 is still under investigation.

GENERAL MEASURES OF PERSONALITY AND PSYCHOPATHOLOGY

The Minnesota Multiphasic Personality Inventory-2

The Minnesota Multiphasic Personality Inventory-2 (MMPI-2; Butcher et al., 2001) is the most widely used measure of psychopathology and personality structure. It consists of 567 statements to which individuals respond true or false. It uses 10 clinical scales to identify various psychological conditions and nine validity scales to assess response styles, as well as various content and supplementary scales (Butcher et al., 2001). It also has a PTSD subscale, called the PTSD–Keane (PK) scale, which was originally designed to assess PTSD among veterans. One of the strengths of the MMPI-2 in PTSD assessment is the presence of validity scales. These validity scales can detect three types of response styles: inconsistent responding, overreporting/exaggeration of symptoms, and underreporting/minimization of symptoms. Administration of the MMPI-2 can be performed in a paper format and in a computerized format. It takes 1 hour to 2 hours to complete and is available in multiple languages. The inventory requires reading at a 6th-grade level. Administration, scoring, and interpretation should be conducted by a trained licensed clinician.

The Personality Assessment Inventory

The Personality Assessment Inventory (PAI) is another multidimensional measure of psychopathology and personality structure that is often used during a trauma/PTSD assessment (Morey, 2007). It consists of 344 items that the individual rates as "totally false," "slightly true," "mainly true," or "very true." The PAI consists of 22 nonoverlapping scales that include four validity scales, 11 clinical scales, five treatment consideration scales, and two interpersonal scales. The clinical scales correspond to the *DSM-IV* diagnostic categories, and the validity scales provide indices of the individual's response style (e.g., faking good, faking bad, defensiveness, or exaggeration).

The PAI also has a PTSD subscale and requires a reading level of 4th to 6th grade. The PAI takes approximately 50 minutes to complete. Administration, scoring, and interpretation should be conducted by a trained licensed clinician. The PAI provides norms for college, clinical, and census purposes and has demonstrated good validity and clinical utility in detecting those who are feigning PTSD (Lange et al., 2010; McDevitt-Murphy et al., 2007; Scragg et al., 2000).

SUMMARY

The assessment of PTSD requires the development of a strong therapeutic alliance with the client. A multimethod approach to assessment that incorporates a clinical interview, self-report measures, and personality inventories is highly recommended. The diagnosis of PTSD requires exposure to a *DSM-5* criterion A traumatic event and the development of symptoms of intrusion, avoidance, negative alterations in cognition and mood, and alterations in arousal and reactivity.

Given the challenges in assessing PTSD, broad-based measures of psychiatric symptoms and personality structures are highly recommended as part of a multimethod approach. These measures not only allow for the assessment of PTSD symptoms, but also provide a way to detect co-occurring psychiatric and personality pathology. Reliable and valid structured interviews designed for the assessment of PTSD include the CAPS, the SCID–PTSD module, and the PSS-I. Clinical interviews can be augmented by the administration of self-report questionnaires, such as the PTSD checklist, and personality tests, such as the MMPI-2 or PAI. The differential diagnosis of PTSD can be challenging in the presence of co-occurring mood, anxiety, or substance use disorders, complicating the diagnostic picture.

NOTE

1. For additional self-report measures, visit the National Center for PTSD at www.ptsd.va.gov/professional/pages/assessments/assessment.asp.

REFERENCES

Adkins, J. W., Weathers, F. W., McDevitt-Murphy, M., & Daniels, J. B. (2008). Psychometric properties of seven self-report measures of posttraumatic stress disorder in college students with mixed civilian trauma exposure. *Journal of Anxiety Disorders, 2,* 1393–1402.

American Psychiatric Association. (1980). *Diagnostic and statistical manual of mental disorders* (3rd ed.). Washington, DC: Author.

American Psychiatric Association. (1987). *Diagnostic and statistical manual of mental disorders* (3rd ed., revision). Washington, DC: Author.

American Psychiatric Association. (1994). *Diagnostic and statistical manual of mental disorders* (4th ed.). Washington, DC: Author.

American Psychiatric Association. (2000). *Diagnostic and statistical manual of mental disorders* (4th ed., text revision). Washington, DC: Author.

American Psychiatric Association. (2013). *Diagnostic and statistical manual of mental disorders* (5th ed.). Washington, DC: Author.

American Psychological Association, Division 56 (Trauma Psychology) (2012). *Guidelines for the assessment of trauma in adults.* Unpublished manuscript.

Arbisi, P. A., Ben-Porath, Y. S., & McNulty, J. (2006). The ability of the MMPI-2 to detect feigned PTSD within the context of compensation seeking. *Psychological Services, 3,* 249–261.

Blake, D. D., Weathers, F. W., Nagy, L. M., Kaloupek, D., Klauminzer, G., Charney, D. S., . . . Buckley, T. C. (2000). *Clinician-Administered PTSD Scale (CAPS) Instruction Manual.* Boston, MA: National Center for PTSD.

Blake, D. D., Weathers, F. W., Nagy, L. M., Kaloupek, D. G., Gusman, F. D., Charney, D. S., & Keane, T. M. (1995). The development of a clinician-administered PTSD scale. *Journal of Traumatic Stress, 8*(1), 75–90.

Bonanno, G. A. (2004). Loss, trauma, and human resilience: Have we underestimated the human capacity to thrive after extremely adverse events? *American Psychologist, 59,* 20–28.

Breslau, N., & Kessler, R. C. (2001). The stressor criterion in *DSM-IV* posttraumatic stress disorder: An empirical investigation. *Biological Psychiatry, 50*(9), 699–704.

Brewin, C. R., Lanius, R. A., Novac, A., Schnyder, U., & Galea, S. (2009). Reformulating PTSD for *DSM-V*: Life after criterion A. *Journal of Traumatic Stress, 22*(5), 366–373.

Briere, J. (1996). Psychometric review of Trauma Symptom Inventory (TSI). In B. H. Stamm (Ed.), *Measurement of stress, trauma, and adaptation* (pp. 381–383). Lutherville, MD: Sidran Press.

Briere, J. (2011). *Trauma Symptom Inventory-2 (TSI-2) professional manual.* Odessa, FL: Psychological Assessment Resources.

Briere, J., Elliott, D. M., Harris, K., & Cotman, A. (1995). Trauma Symptom Inventory: Psychometrics and association with childhood and adult trauma in clinical samples. *Journal of Interpersonal Violence, 10,* 387–401.

Briere, J. N., & Scott, C. (2012). *Principles of trauma therapy: A guide to symptoms, evaluation, and treatment* (2nd ed.). Washington, DC: Sage.

Bryant, R. A., Friedman, M. J., Spiegel, D., Ursano, R., & Strain, J. (2011). A review of acute stress disorder in *DSM-5. Depression and Anxiety, 28*(9), 802–817.

Butcher, J. N., Graham, J. R., Ben-Porath, Y. S., Tellegen, A., Dahlstrom, W. G., & Kaemmer, B. (2001). *MMPI-2 manual for administration, scoring, and interpretation.* Minneapolis: University of Minnesota Press.

Cloitre, M., Courtois, C. A., Charuvastra, A., Stolbach, B. C., & Green, B. L. (2011). Treatment of complex PTSD: Results of the ISTSS expert clinician survey on best practices. *Journal of Traumatic Stress, 24*(6), 615–627.

Colangelo, J. J. (2009). The recovered memory controversy: A representative case study. *Journal of Child Sexual Abuse, 18*(1), 103–121.

De Jong, J. T., Komproe, I. H., & Van Ommeren, M. (2003). Common mental disorders in postconflict settings. *The Lancet, 361*(9375), 2128–2130.

Elhai, J. D., Gray, M. J., Kashdan, T. B., & Franklin, C. L. (2005). Which instruments are most commonly used to assess traumatic event exposure and posttraumatic effects? A survey of traumatic stress professionals. *Journal of Traumatic Stress, 18*(5), 541–545.

First, M. B., Spitzer, R. L., Gibbon, M., & Williams, J. B. W. (2002). *Structured Clinical Interview for* DSM-IV-TR *Axis I Disorders, Research Version, Patient Edition (SCID-I/P).* New York, NY: Biometrics Research, New York State Psychiatric Institute.

Foa, E., Cashman, L., Jaycox, L., & Perry, K. (1997). The validation of a self-report measure of PTSD: The Posttraumatic Diagnostic Scale. *Psychological Assessment, 9*, 445–451.

Foa, E. B., Hembree, E. A., Cahill, S. P., Rauch., S. A. M., Riggs, D. S., Feeny, N. C., & Yadin, E. (2005) Randomized trial of prolonged exposure for PTSD with and without cognitive restructuring outcome at academic and community clinics. *Journal of Consulting and Clinical Psychology, 73*, 953–964.

Foa, E. B., Riggs, D., Dancu, C., & Rothbaum, B. (1993). Reliability and validity of a brief instrument for assessing post-traumatic stress disorder. *Journal of Traumatic Stress, 6*, 459–474.

Foa, E. B., & Tolin, D. F. (2000). Comparison of the PTSD Symptom Scale–Interview Version and the Clinician-Administered PTSD Scale. *Journal of Traumatic Stress, 13*, 181–191.

Friedman, M. J., Keane, T. M., & Resick, P. (Eds.). (2007). *Handbook of PTSD: Science and practice.* New York, NY: The Guilford Press.

Friedman, M. J., Resick, P., & Keane, T. M. (2007). PTSD: Twenty-five years of progress and challenges. In M. J. Friedman, T. M. Keane, & P. Resick (Eds.), *Handbook of PTSD: Science and practice* (pp. 3–18). New York, NY: The Guilford Press.

Griffin, M. G., Uhlmansiek, M. H., Resick, P. A., & Mechanic, M. B. (2004). Comparison of the Posttraumatic Stress Disorder Scale versus the Clinician-Administered Posttraumatic Stress Disorder Scale in domestic violence survivors. *Journal of Traumatic Stress, 17*(6), 497–503.

Herman, J. L. (1992). Complex PTSD: A syndrome in survivors of prolonged and repeated trauma. *Journal of Traumatic Stress, 5*(3), 377–391.

Keane, T. M., Brief, D. J., Pratt, E. M., & Miller, M. W. (2007). Assessment of PTSD and its comorbidities in adults. In M. J. Friedman, T. M. Keane, & P. Resick (Eds.), *Handbook of PTSD: Science and practice* (pp. 279–305). New York, NY: The Guilford Press.

Keen, S. M., Kutter, C. J., Niles, B. L., & Krinsley, K. R. (2008). Psychometric properties of the PTSD checklist in a sample of male veterans. *Journal of Rehabilitation Research and Development, 45*, 465–474.

Kilpatrick, D. G., Resnick, H. S., & Acierno, R. E. (2009). Should PTSD criterion A be retained? *Journal of Traumatic Stress, 22*(5), 374–383.

Lange, R. T., Sullivan, K. A., & Scott, C. (2010). Comparison of MMPI-2 and PAI validity indicators to detect feigned depression and PTSD symptom reporting. *Psychiatry Research, 176*(2), 229–235.

Lobbestael, J., Leurgans, M., & Arntz, A. (2011). Inter-rater reliability of the Structured Clinical Interview for *DSM-IV* Axis I Disorders (SCID I) and Axis II Disorders (SCID II). *Clinical Psychology and Psychotherapy, 18*(1), 75–79.

McDevitt-Murphy, M. E., Weathers, F. W., Flood, A. M., Eakin, D. E., & Benson, T. A. (2007). The utility of the PAI and the MMPI-2 for discriminating PTSD, depression, and social phobia in trauma-exposed college students. *Assessment, 14*(2), 181–195.

McDonald, S. D., & Calhoun, P. S. (2010). The diagnostic accuracy of the PTSD checklist: A critical review. *Clinical Psychology Review, 30*(8), 976–987.

McNally, R. J. (2003). Progress and controversy in the study of posttraumatic stress disorder. *Annual Review of Psychology, 54*, 229–252.

Morey, L. C. (2007). *Personality Assessment Inventory professional manual* (2nd ed.). Lutz, FL: Psychological Assessment Resources.

Pelcovitz, D., Van der Kolk, B. A., Roth, S., Mandel, F., Kaplan, S., & Resick, P. (1997). Development of a criteria set and a structured interview for disorders of extreme stress (SIDES). *Journal of Traumatic Stress, 10*(1), 3–16.

Powers, M. B., Gillihan, S. J., Rosenfield, D., Jerud, A. B., & Foa, E. B. (2012). Reliability and validity of the PDS and PSS-I among participants with PTSD and alcohol dependence. *Journal of Anxiety Disorders, 26*(5), 617–623.

Resick, P. A., Bovin, M. J., Calloway, A. L., Dick, A. M., King, M. W., Mitchell, K. S., . . . Wolf, E. J. (2012). A critical evaluation of the complex PTSD literature: Implications for *DSM-5*. *Journal of Traumatic Stress, 25*, 241–251.

Resnick, P. J., West, S., & Payne, J. W. (2008). Malingering of posttraumatic disorders. In R. Rogers, *Clinical assessment of malingering and deception* (3rd ed., pp. 109–127). New York, NY: Guilford Press.

Ruggiero, K. J., Del Ben, K., Scotti, J. R., & Rabalais, A. E. (2003). Psychometric properties of the PTSD Checklist–Civilian Version. *Journal of Traumatic Stress, 16*(5), 495–502.

Schillaci, J., Yanasak, E., Adams, J. H., Dunn, N. J., Rehm, L. P., & Hamilton, J. D. (2009). Guidelines for differential diagnoses in a population with posttraumatic stress disorder. *Professional Psychology: Research and Practice, 40*(1), 39–45.

Scragg, P., Bor, R., & Mendham, M. (2000). Assessment: Feigning posttraumatic stress disorder on the PAI. *Clinical Psychology and Psychotherapy, 7*, 155–160.

Spitzer, R. L., First, M. B., & Wakefield, J. C. (2007). Saving PTSD from itself in *DSM-V. Journal of Anxiety Disorders, 21*(2), 233–241.

Weathers, F. W., Blake, D. D., Schnurr, P. P., Kaloupek, D. G., Marx, B. P., & Keane, T. M. (2013a). *The Clinician-Administered PTSD Scale for DSM-5 (CAPS-5).* Interview available from the National Center for PTSD at www.ptsd.va.gov

Weathers, F. W., Blake, D. D., Schnurr, P. P., Kaloupek, D. G., Marx, B. P., & Keane, T. M. (2013b). *The Life Events Checklist for DSM-5 (LEC-5).* Instrument available from the National Center for PTSD at www.ptsd.va.gov

Weathers, F. W., & Keane, T. M. (2007). The criterion A problem revisited: Controversies and challenges in defining and measuring psychological trauma. *Journal of Traumatic Stress, 20*(5), 915–916.

Weathers, F. W., Keane, T. M., & Davidson, J. (2001). Clinician-administered PTSD scale: A review of the first ten years of research. *Depression and Anxiety, 13*, 132–156.

Weathers, F. W., Litz, B. T., Huska, J. A., & Keane, T. M. (1994). *The PTSD Checklist–Civilian Version (PCLC).* Boston, MA: National Center for PTSD.

Zanarini, M. C., Skodol, A. E., Bender, D., Dolan, R., Sanislow, C., Schaefer, E., . . . Gunderson, J. G. (2000). The Collaborative Longitudinal Personality Disorders Study: Reliability of axis I and II diagnoses. *Journal of Personality Disorders, 14*(4), 291–299.

Trauma and Health

sychological trauma can have long-term effects on health. When considering the impact of trauma on health, most people tend to focus on immediate consequences, such as injury. And these needs can be substantial. For example, in the National Violence Against Women Survey, 39% of women who were victims of violence reported injuries. More than 500,000 women sought medical care for their injuries, and 62% of these women were seen in emergency departments (Tjaden & Thoennes, 2000). It is safe to say that trauma-related injuries cause massive demands on the health care system.

Increasingly, however, researchers have discovered that injuries represent the tip of the iceberg in terms of health effects. Recent studies have revealed a relationship between trauma and chronic diseases, such as heart disease; diabetes; pulmonary diseases, such as emphysema; chronic pain syndromes, such as irritable bowel syndrome and fibromyalgia; and autoimmune disease. Many of these diseases are common and can lead to premature mortality (Felitti et al., 1998; Kendall-Tackett, 2013; Shonkoff, Boyce, & McEwen, 2009). Indeed, it is likely that the long-term health effects of trauma surpass the numbers of people who are seeking assistance for current injuries.

THE EFFECTS OF ADVERSE CHILDHOOD EXPERIENCES

Childhood adversity, for example, has been related to a wide range of chronic diseases and conditions. In the Adverse Childhood Experiences (ACE) study, a study of more than 17,000 patients in the Kaiser Permanente system, the more types of childhood adversity that patients reported, the worse their health was as adults (Felitti et al., 1998). Patients who reported four or more types of childhood adversity, including sexual, physical, and emotional abuse; exposure to domestic violence; and parental mental illness, criminal activity, and substance abuse, were at significantly increased risk for such diverse conditions as ischemic heart disease, cancer, stroke, chronic bronchitis, emphysema, diabetes, skeletal fractures, and hepatitis.

Trauma in childhood appears to be common. Dong and colleagues analyzed data from 8,629 adult members of an HMO (Dong et al., 2004). The researchers found that two-thirds of their participants reported at least one ACE. Among those who experienced at least one ACE, 81% to 98% had experienced more than one. Most had experienced from two to four other types.

In a study of 163 male and female psychiatric patients over the age of 50, Talbot and colleagues (Talbot et al., 2009) found that patients who had been raped as children had more medical conditions, worse physical functioning, and more pain than patients who had not been sexually assaulted. In terms of overall medical conditions, the effect of rape was comparable to adding 8 years of chronological age. In terms of activities of daily living and bodily pain, rape in childhood was comparable to adding 20 years of chronological age. The authors recommended that practitioners screen for possible abuse histories, because early detection might help prevent some of these illnesses from occurring.

PTSD following a man-made disaster showed similar health effects (Dirkzwager, van der Velden, Grievink, & Yzermans, 2007). In this study, 896 survivors of a man-made disaster were surveyed at 3 weeks and at 18 months after the disaster. The authors found that PTSD was associated with physician-reported vascular, musculoskeletal, and dermatological problems. PTSD also increased the risk of new vascular problems. These problems appeared even after controlling for previous health problems, smoking, and demographic characteristics.

Following is a brief summary of research on some of the major health problems that are common among trauma survivors.

Cardiovascular Disease

The Canadian Community Health Survey (N = 36,984) revealed that 1% (N = 478) of participants had a formal diagnosis of PTSD (Sareen et al., 2007). Hypertension and heart disease; asthma and chronic obstructive pulmonary disease, such as emphysema; chronic pain, including fibromyalgia, arthritis, and migraine; ulcerative colitis and ulcers; and cancer all occurred in higher rates among participants with PTSD compared with others in the sample. PTSD was also associated with suicide attempts, poor quality of life, and short- and long-term disability. The authors concluded that these health effects were above and beyond the effects of depression or other mental disorders and were the unique contribution of PTSD.

Researchers found that a history of childhood abuse increased the risk of cardiovascular disease in the National Comorbidity Survey (Batten, Aslan, Maciejewski, & Mazure, 2004). This link was especially strong for women, with maltreated women having a ninefold increase in cardiovascular disease compared to nonmaltreated women, even after controlling for the effects of depression.

A recent meta-analysis of 24 studies ($N = 48{,}801$) found that physical and sexual child abuse increased the risk for cardiovascular problems, such as heart attack and stroke (Wegman & Stetler, 2009). In addition, adults who experienced childhood abuse were also at increased risk for adult-onset migraines, broken bones, arthritis, diabetes, obesity, asthma, bronchitis, neurological and musculoskeletal conditions, respiratory problems, gastrointestinal conditions, and metabolic disorders. Women appeared to be at higher risk for these health effects, but males were underrepresented in the literature.

Diabetes

Trauma is seldom considered as a possible cause for diabetes. But recent studies have found that there is a relationship, particularly for trauma that occurred in childhood (Felitti et al., 1998; Wegman & Stetler, 2009). Rich-Edwards and colleagues (2010) found that child or adolescent physical and sexual abuse dramatically increased the risk of type 2 diabetes, even after adjusting for age, race, body type at 5 years, parental education, and parental history of diabetes (Rich-Edwards et al., 2010). Using data from the Nurses' Health Study II, they found that severe physical abuse increased the risk of type 2 diabetes by 50%, and severe sexual abuse (repeated forced sex) increased the risk by 69%. There was a dose–response effect: The more severe the abuse, the more severe the symptoms. There was also an additive effect: Women who were both physically and sexually abused were at higher risk than those who experienced only one type of abuse.

Adult body mass index (BMI) was also influenced by past abuse (Rich-Edwards et al., 2010). Girls with a history of physical or sexual abuse had higher BMIs than nonabused girls. Furthermore, the trajectories of weight gain were steeper for abused girls. In other words, these girls started with higher BMIs as children and gained weight more rapidly than their nonabused peers.

Pulmonary Conditions

Trauma, particularly childhood trauma, also increases the risk of pulmonary conditions. For example, childhood adversity was also related to adult-onset asthma (Scott et al., 2008). The authors summarized the findings of 10 cross-sectional population surveys of adults (N = 18,303). Suglia and colleagues (Suglia, Ryan, Laden, Dockery, & Wright, 2008) found that girls who were exposed to high levels of parental verbal aggression had decreased lung function in their study of 313 urban children. These findings still appear even after adjusting for maternal education, child's age and race, tobacco exposure, and respiratory conditions, such as asthma, allergies, and respiratory infections. There was not a significant relationship between lung function and parental verbal aggression for boys. Conversely, boys had decreased lung function when exposed to community violence, but girls did not. Boys with the highest levels of exposure to community violence had the poorest lung function.

Somatic Complaints

Childhood physical and sexual abuse increased the risk of somatic complaints in a study of 3,568 randomly sampled insured women aged 18–64 (Bonomi, Cannon, Anderson, & Rivara, 2008). The effects of physical and sexual abuse were additive. Women who were both physically and sexually abused before the age of 18 reported significantly more joint pain, insomnia, fatigue, stomach ache, abdominal pain, severe headaches, numb hands or feet, diarrhea, constipation, shortness of breath, facial pain, dizziness, nausea, vomiting, and chest pain. Depression was also common: Women who had experienced both types of abuse had triple the risk.

In mainland China, a study of high school students (N = 6,593) found that physical and sexual abuse was associated with higher levels of a number of physical symptoms, including stomach pain, nightmares, poor appetite, shortness of breath, chest pain, dizziness, irregular menstruation, and suicidal ideation (Wong et al., 2009). Severe abuse led to more intense symptoms. And in this study, boys were more likely to experience severe physical and sexual abuse than girls.

Sachs-Ericsson and colleagues (Sachs-Ericsson, Kendall-Tackett, & Hernandez, 2007), using data from the National Comorbidity Survey, noted that subjects with a history of either physical or sexual child abuse or intimate partner violence were more likely to report pain when describing their current health symptoms. Leserman and Drossman (2007) found that patients with a history of physical or sexual abuse in childhood or of intimate partner violence as adults had 1.5 to 2 times the risk of reporting gastrointestinal symptoms or having a functional gastrointestinal disorder.

Golding (1994) also found that women who had been sexually assaulted as either children or adults had significantly more health problems than did their nonassaulted counterparts. The women were at increased risk for diabetes, arthritis, and physical disability. When controlling for demographic characteristics, the odds of having at least six symptoms were 3 times greater for the assaulted women. Pain symptoms were more likely, as were neurological symptoms, such as loss of voice, fainting, trouble walking, or paralysis.

Autoimmune Disease

Data from the ACE study found that cumulative childhood stress and a higher ACE score increased the risk of being hospitalized with a diagnosed autoimmune disease (Dube et al., 2009). Compared to people with no ACEs, a person with two or more ACEs was at 80% increased risk for diseases, such as multiple sclerosis, Graves disease, and celiac disease; 100% increased risk for rheumatic diseases, such as lupus, rheumatoid arthritis, and scleroderma; and 70% increased risk for diseases, such as insulin-dependent diabetes mellitus, irritable bowel syndrome, and idiopathic myocarditis. The authors concluded that traumatic stress, particularly in childhood, increased the likelihood of hospitalization with a diagnosed autoimmune disease decades later.

PATTERNS OF HEALTH CARE USE

With higher rates of illness and somatic complaints, it should not surprise us to learn that people who have experienced trauma have high rates of health care use. Trauma survivors see primary care physicians more often and are more likely to see specialists and go to the emergency department. When asked about their health at health care visits, they report more symptoms on a review of systems (a list of symptoms related to all parts of the body), undergo more procedures and diagnostic tests, and have surgery more often (Kendall-Tackett, Marshall, & Ness, 2000). Yet they are often very unhappy with the care they receive and may be retraumatized by their health care providers.

Use of Health Care Services

In a study of women seeking health care at Veterans Affairs (VA) facilities ($N = 2,578$), 33% ($N = 858$) screened positive for PTSD (Dobie et al., 2006). The women with PTSD had more outpatient visits to the emergency department, primary care, medical or surgery subspecialties, ancillary services, and diagnostic tests. Similarly, in a large primary care practice, women who had been sexually abused reported significantly more symptoms and a greater intensity of symptoms than did their nonabused counterparts (Hulme, 2000).

Felitti (1991) found that 22% of women who had been sexually abused had visited a doctor 10 or more times a year, compared with 6% of the control group; this was considered to be a pattern of high health care use. And Finestone et al. (2000)

found that women in a support group for sexual abuse survivors reported more pain and went to their family practitioners more often than did the women in the comparison groups.

Hospitalization and Surgery

Trauma survivors also have surgery and are hospitalized more often. In one primary care sample, men and women who reported physical or sexual child abuse or domestic violence as adults had twice as many surgeries as their nonabused counterparts (Kendall-Tackett et al., 2000). In two studies of patients with chronic pain, those with a history of physical or sexual abuse had significantly more surgeries than did their nonabused counterparts (Domino & Haber, 1987; Drossman et al., 1990). Hulme (2000) also found that abuse survivors had higher numbers of surgeries. In a case study of seven women who had been sexually abused as children, Arnold, Rogers, and Cook (1990) found a mean of eight surgeries per patient.

In a sample of women seeking care at the VA, women with PTSD had significantly higher rates of hospitalizations and surgical procedures (Dobie et al., 2006). The mean number of days in the hospital per year was 43.4 for women with PTSD and 17 for women without PTSD. Women with PTSD were more likely to have a service-related disability. They were also more likely to have a chronic pain syndrome, such as irritable bowel syndrome and fibromyalgia. And they had significantly higher BMIs. Seventy-five percent of the women with PTSD also had depression, and they were more likely to smoke and to abuse alcohol.

Women in a support group for sexual abuse survivors reported more hospitalizations compared to a sample of nurses and non-abused women who were psychiatric outpatients (Finestone et al., 2000). Finally, in a study of women with chronic headaches, 76% of the women with a history of physical or sexual abuse had been hospitalized compared with 25% of the nonabused women (Domino & Haber, 1987).

Increased Health Care Costs

When men and women go to the doctor more often, and have more surgeries, their health care costs increase. Not surprisingly, trauma is associated with increased health care costs. For example, George Washington University estimates that veterans with PTSD cost the health care system 3.5 times as much as veterans without PTSD and that the U.S. government has spent $2 billion so far to treat Iraq and Afghanistan veterans with PTSD (Face the Facts USA, 2013). The costs of child maltreatment are equally high. In a recent analysis, the estimated lifetime cost per victim is $210,012 in 2010 dollars (Fang, Brown, Florence, & Mercy, 2012). This includes $32,648 health care costs incurred during childhood, $10,530 in adult medical costs, and $144,360 in lost productivity.

Depression is a common co-occurring symptom in trauma survivors. According to a recent analysis, depression has a number of significant costs associated with it (Kessler, 2012). These include low marital satisfaction, low work performance, and low earnings. It is also associated with a number of health conditions, such as heart disease, diabetes, and chronic pain. Finally, depression is even associated with early mortality. The National Alliance on Mental Illness estimates that the workplace costs of depression total $34 billion per year in direct and indirect costs. These include more annual sick days, higher rates of short-term disability, and lower productivity when on the job (National Alliance on Mental Illness, 2013).

Chronic pain syndromes are common in trauma survivors, and they too are costly. According to the U.S. Institute of Medicine, chronic pain costs between $560 billion and $635 billion a year in health care costs and affects 116 million Americans (Committee on Advancing Pain Research & Medicine, 2011). Chronic pain patients are 5 times more likely to use health care services than are patients without chronic pain (Becker et al., 1997) Furthermore, one in four sick days is taken for pain, totaling 50 million workdays lost per year (Brownlee & Schrof, 1997).

WHY TRAUMA MAKES PEOPLE SICK

As we have seen, health problems occur more frequently among trauma survivors. Trauma does indeed make people sick, which raises the intriguing question of why it occurs. Health is complicated, as are the forces that influence it. We cannot hope to improve the health of trauma survivors if we continue in the mindset of treating mental health and physical health separately. Rather, we should strive to create prevention and treatment models that address all five pathways. Only by recognizing, and addressing, all these underlying factors can we hope to improve the health trauma survivors.

Following is a brief description of five possible pathways by which trauma can influence health. The five pathways are physiological, behavioral, social, cognitive, and emotional, drawing from the literature in health psychology (Kendall-Tackett, 2013). These five pathways point to possible mechanisms by which trauma can lead to health problems. Trauma survivors can be influenced by any or all of these.

Physiological Pathways

Trauma changes the body. The sympathetic nervous system becomes more reactive. Levels of stress hormones and inflammatory cytokines become dysregulated. The upregulation of the inflammatory cytokines is a particular possible explanation for the increase in disease in trauma survivors. Cytokines are proteins that regulate immune response. They help the body heal wounds and fight infection by stimulating an inflammatory response. When an acute response, inflammation is adaptive and helps us survive. However, when the inflammatory response is chronically upregulated, it can increase the risk of a wide range of illnesses, including heart disease, diabetes, Alzheimer's disease, and even cancer (Batten et al., 2004; Robles, Glaser, & Kiecolt-Glaser, 2005; Suarez, 2006).

Another physiological effect of trauma is that pain thresholds are often lower, which increases the risk of chronic pain syndromes in trauma survivors. Threshold refers to the magnitude of sensation necessary for it to be perceived. Someone with a lower pain threshold is hypersensitive and will perceive pain even when lightly touched. Some consider this hypersensitivity a major evolutionary advantage because it alerts people to potential danger. However, there is a significant downside to a lowered pain threshold in day-to-day life because normal physical sensations are perceived as painful (Woolf & Salter, 2000).

Children are especially vulnerable to traumatic stress due to the malleability of children's brains and neurological systems during the first 5 years of life (DeBellis, 2011; Heim & Nemeroff, 2009). The effects of trauma are more likely to be pervasive if the trauma occurs younger than age 5.

Behavioral Pathways

This pathway has the most empirical support, because most researchers who are interested in why trauma leads to health problems focus on health-compromising behaviors. And they do indeed exist. Trauma survivors are overrepresented in populations that participate in high-risk activities, such as substance abuse, certain sexual behavior, smoking, eating disorders, and attempted suicide (Anda et al., 2008; Brodsky & Stanley, 2008; Holzer, Uppala, Wonderlich, Crosby, & Simonich, 2008; Messman-Moore, Coates, Gaffey, & Johnson, 2008).

Substance abuse is a common symptom among trauma survivors, and among populations who abuse substances, there are high percentages of trauma survivors (Conroy, Degenhardt, Mattick, & Nelson, 2009; Tucci, Kerr-Correa, & Souza-Formigoni, 2010). High-risk sexual activity is another well-documented sequela of trauma. This includes early initiation into consensual sexual activity, many sexual partners, and risky sexual practices (e.g., no condom and no contraception; Munroe, Kibler, Ma, Dollar, & Coleman, 2010; Steel & Herlitz, 2005).

Cognitive Pathways

Trauma survivors were more likely to have negative beliefs about themselves and others. Cognitions have a key role in health but are often overlooked as a cause of health problems. Cognitions can explain some of the difficulties that otherwise high-functioning trauma survivors face.

Negative beliefs can be about self or others. An example of a negative belief about self that is associated with trauma includes shame. Trauma survivors may have a sense of shame about what happened to them or about themselves, and they may conclude that they have lost social value (Dickerson, Kemeny, Aziz, Kim, & Fahey, 2004). Left unchecked, shame can cause depression, interpersonal difficulties, and avoidance behaviors, including substance abuse. It can even increase vulnerability to revictimization (Persons, Kershaw, Sikkema, & Hansen, 2010).

Negative beliefs about others are also related to health problems. One of the most studied negative beliefs about others is hostility. For people with a hostile worldview, life is not benign. People high in hostility do not trust others, are suspicious and cynical about human nature, and tend to interpret the actions of others as aggressive (Smith, 1992). And hostility is a common, and frankly understandable, response among trauma survivors. In a sample from primary care, 52% of female sexual abuse survivors indicated that they could not trust others, compared with 17% of the nonabused women (Hulme, 2000). Among a sample of 90 women veterans (Butterfield, Forneris, Feldman, & Beckham, 2000), women with PTSD reported significantly higher levels of hostility, and had poorer health, than women without PTSD.

Negative beliefs can undermine health and may also lead to harmful behaviors and harmful relationships. And yet health care providers often don't take these beliefs as seriously as they should, because they are not as dramatic as harmful behaviors.

Nevertheless, the detrimental effects are very real. For example, hostility has been implicated in heart disease, metabolic syndrome, and diabetes (Kendall-Tackett, 2007, 2010), and should be addressed if the health effects of trauma are to be affected.

Social Pathways

Human beings are meant to have social relationships with others. When they do not, there are physical consequences. Recent neuroscience research has found that our bodies process threats to our relationships as threats to our survival (Jenson-Campbell & MacDonald, 2011). Unfortunately, trauma survivors often have difficulties in their relationships. Some examples include divorce, marital disruptions, and social isolation (MacDonald, Borsook, & Spielmann, 2011; Sandberg, Suess, & Heaton, 2010).

One of the more extreme manifestations of this is revictimization. Unfortunately, people who have experienced childhood trauma, in particular, have increased vulnerability to later victimization by intimate partners or in work or therapy settings (Gagne, Lavoie, & Hebert, 2005; Messman-Moore & Brown, 2004; Teegan, 1999).

In addition, trauma survivors are more likely to be poor, struggle in school, and be homeless than their nontraumatized counterparts (Ferguson, 2009; Kendall-Tackett & Eckenrode, 1996; O'Leary, Coohey, & Easton, 2010). This seems to be especially true when trauma survivors have PTSD. Even behavior that we might label as "codependent" can be the result of previous trauma (Helgeson & Fritz, 1998). And all these social difficulties can negatively affect health.

Emotional Pathways

Depression and PTSD are common sequelae of trauma. Depression is one of the most commonly occurring sequelae of trauma (Kendall-Tackett, 2013). But it is one that is thought of as an outcome—an endpoint we measure in the wake of traumatic

63

events. Yet depression can also be a mechanism that leads to poor health. The negative effects of depression are well known in the cardiovascular literature. Patients who become depressed after a heart attack are two to three times more likely to have another heart attack and are three to four times more likely to die (Lesperance & Frasure-Smith, 2000). A chronically upregulated inflammatory response system in trauma survivors is the likely culprit (Kendall-Tackett, 2010; Kiecolt-Glaser et al., 2007; Kop & Gottdiener, 2005).

In depressed people, there are several biomarkers of increased inflammation, including acute-phase proteins, such as C-reactive protein (CRP; Kop & Gottdiener, 2005; Robles et al., 2005) and proinflammatory cytokines. The proinflammatory cytokines that have been most consistently identified in studies of depressed people are abnormal levels of the normally present biochemicals interleukin-1β (IL-1β), interleukin-6 (IL-6), tumor necrosis factor-α (TNF-α), and interferon-γ (IFN-γ; Kiecolt-Glaser et al., 2007; Robles et al., 2005). Researchers hypothesize that chronic inflammation increases the risk of heart disease by damaging blood vessels, reducing the stability of plaque, and increasing the risk of acute episodes (Kop & Gottdiener, 2005).

Recent research has revealed similar negative health consequences for PTSD (Danese et al., 2009; Danese, Pariante, Caspi, Taylor, & Poulton, 2007). We're used to thinking about PTSD and depression as outcomes, but we also need to think of them as mechanisms that can lead to poor health.

HEALTH CARE PROVIDERS' RESPONSE TO TRAUMA SURVIVORS

Trauma survivors come into a health care system that is often not prepared to receive them. Providers often do not know what to do with or for them. In addition, there is rarely infrastructure in place for providers to make referrals. Finally, trauma survivors often have vague symptoms that come and go, and they may be labeled as "difficult" by their providers.

A recent study of primary care providers found that many felt unprepared to deal with psychological trauma (Green et al., 2011). This study included a focus group of 31 primary providers who worked with a low-income, underserved population. They reported frequent contact with patients who had trauma histories. However, many indicated that they felt unprepared to deal with these patients. When asked to describe some "difficult" patients, they mentioned patients with mental illness or substance abuse. The physicians also had issues with patients with multiple, complex, or vague physical complaints, chronic pain, or obesity—in other words, the profile of many trauma survivors in the health care system. There were two main concerns: the physicians' lack of formal training in how to care for trauma survivors and their strong emotional reactions to some of these patients. By being less effective, the health care providers felt that working with trauma patients was contributing to their job stress. The authors suggested that additional training and appropriate treatment models could increase both the providers' effectiveness and their job satisfaction.

Some of the difficulties health care providers have with trauma patients may be due to their own experiences. The percentage of health care providers who are also abuse survivors appears to be higher than it is in the general population. For example, in data from the Nurses' Health Study II ($N = 67,853$), 54% indicated that they had experienced physical abuse in child- or adulthood. In addition, 34% reported sexual abuse as a child or adolescent (Rich-Edwards et al., 2010).

A study of 176 hospital-based health care workers in Canada found that 68% had a history of one or more types of violence, abuse, or neglect: 33% before the age of 13 (Maunder, Peladeau, Savage, & Lancee, 2010). Health care workers with abuse histories reported more recent stressful life events (11 versus five over the previous 6 months) and greater psychological distress than reported by those who were not abused. Childhood adversity was also associated with more missed work days and lower perceived social support. The authors concluded that childhood adversity is common among health care workers and is associated with a higher number of life events, more psychological distress, and greater impairment.

Health care providers are not the only professional group with high rates of past abuse. In a study of urban development workers, 75% reported direct community violence victimization, 71% reported at least one ACE, and 14% met the diagnostic criteria for PTSD (Walling, Eriksson, Putman, & Foy, 2011). Urban development workers choose to live and work in impoverished neighborhoods with the goal of improving quality of life for underserved communities. Most of the organizations whose workers were included in this sample were faith based. The most common ACEs they reported were parental separation or divorce, substance abuse in the household, mental illness in the household, and sexual abuse.

SUMMARY

Trauma survivors often face substantial health issues that are directly, or indirectly, due to the trauma they experienced. Unfortunately, they often come into a health care system that is not trauma informed and that is ill-equipped to handle the often complicated health problems that are common in trauma survivors. Although there has been some move to make the health care system more responsive to the needs of trauma survivors, this population remains largely underserved. Given the serious—often life-threatening—conditions that trauma survivors often have, an adequate health care system response is perhaps the most pressing need of survivors of traumatic events.

REFERENCES

Anda, R. F., Brown, D. W., Dube, S. R., Bremner, J. D., Felitti, V. J., & Giles, W. H. (2008). Adverse childhood experiences and chronic obstructive pulmonary disease in adults. *American Journal of Preventive Medicine, 34*(5), 396–403. doi:S0749-3797(08)00151-7 [pii] 10.1016/j.amepre.2008.02.002

Arnold, R. P., Rogers, D., & Cook, D. A. G. (1990). Medical problems of adults who were sexually abused in childhood. *British Medical Journal, 300,* 705–708.

Batten, S. V., Aslan, M., Maciejewski, P. K., & Mazure, C. M. (2004). Childhood maltreatment as a risk factor for adult cardiovascular disease and depression. *Journal of Clinical Psychiatry, 65,* 249–254.

Becker, N., Bondegaard, T. A., Olsen, A. K., Sjogren, P., Bech, P., & Eriksen, J. (1997). Pain epidemiology and health-related quality of life in chronic non-malignant pain patients referred to a Danish multi-disciplinary pain center. *Pain, 73,* 393–400.

Bonomi, A. E., Cannon, E. A., Anderson, M. L., & Rivara, F. P. (2008). Association between self-reported health and physical and/or sexual abuse experienced before age 18. *Child Abuse & Neglect, 32,* 693–701.

Brodsky, B. S., & Stanley, B. (2008). Adverse childhood experiences and suicidal behavior. *Psychiatric Clinics of North America, 31*(2), 223–235. doi:S0193-953X(08)00026-9 [pii] 10.1016/j. psc.2008.02.002

Brownlee, S., & Schrof, J. M. (1997, March 17). The quality of mercy. *U.S. News & World Report,* 54–67.

Butterfield, M. I., Forneris, C. A., Feldman, M. E., & Beckham, J. C. (2000). Hostility and functional health status in women veterans with and without posttraumatic stress disorder: A preliminary study. *Journal of Traumatic Stress, 13,* 735–741.

Committee on Advancing Pain Research & Medicine. (2011). *Relieving pain in America.* Washington, DC: National Academies Press.

Conroy, E., Degenhardt, L., Mattick, R. P., & Nelson, E. C. (2009). Child maltreatment as a risk factor for opioid dependence: Comparison of family characteristics and type and severity of child maltreatment with a matched control group. *Child Abuse & Neglect, 33,* 343–352.

Danese, A., Moffitt, T. E., Harrington, H., Milne, B. J., Polanczyk, G., Pariante, C. M., & Caspi, A. (2009). Adverse childhood experiences and adult risk factors for age-related disease: Depression, inflammation, and clustering of metabolic risk factors. *Archives of Pediatric and Adolescent Medicine, 163*(12), 1135–1143.

Danese, A., Pariante, C. M., Caspi, A., Taylor, A., & Poulton, R. (2007). Childhood maltreatment predicts adult inflammation in a life-course study. *Proceedings of the National Academy of Sciences USA, 104*(4), 1319–1324. doi:0610362104 [pii] 10.1073/pnas.0610362104

DeBellis, M. D. (2011). Neurodevelopmental biology associated with childhood sexual abuse. *Journal of Child Sexual Abuse, 20*, 548–587.

Dickerson, S. S., Kemeny, M. E., Aziz, N., Kim, K. H., & Fahey, J. L. (2004). Immunological effects of induced shame and guilt. *Psychosomatic Medicine, 66*, 124–131.

Dirkzwager, A. J., van der Velden, P. G., Grievink, L., & Yzermans, C. J. (2007). Disaster-related posttraumatic stress disorder and physical health. *Psychosomatic Medicine, 69*(5), 435–440. doi:PSY.0b013e318052e20a [pii] 10.1097/PSY.0b013e318052e20a

Dobie, D. J., Maynard, C., Kivlahan, D. R., Johnson, K. M., Simpson, T., David, A. C., & Bradley, K. (2006). Posttraumatic stress disorder screening status is associated with increased VA medical and surgical utilization in women. *Journal of General Internal Medicine, 21*(Suppl. 3), S58–64. doi:JGI376 [pii] 10.1111/j.1525-1497.2006.00376.x

Domino, J. V., & Haber, J. D. (1987). Prior physical and sexual abuse in women with chronic headache: Clinical correlates. *Headache, 27*, 310–314.

Dong, M., Anda, R. F., Felitti, V. J., Dube, S. R., Williamson, D. F., Thompson, T. J., . . . Giles, W. H. (2004). The interrelatedness of multiple forms of childhood abuse, neglect, and household dysfunction. *Child Abuse & Neglect, 28*(7), 771–784. doi:10.1016/j.chiabu.2004.01.008 S0145213404001486 [pii]

Drossman, D. A., Leserman, J., Nachman, G., Li, Z., Gluck, H., Toomey, T. C., & Mitchell, C. M. (1990). Sexual and physical abuse in women with functional or organic gastrointestinal disorders. *Annals of Internal Medicine, 113*, 828–833.

Dube, S. R., Fairweather, D., Pearson, W. S., Felitti, V. J., Anda, R. F., & Croft, J. B. (2009). Cumulative childhood stress and autoimmune diseases in adults. *Psychosomatic Medicine, 71*(2), 243–250.

Face the Facts USA. (2013). *Shocking PTSD, suicide rates for vets.* Retrieved from http://www.facethefactsusa.org/facts/the-true-price-of-war-in-human-terms

Fang, X., Brown, D. S., Florence, C. S., & Mercy, J. A. (2012). The economic burden of child maltreatment in the United States and implications for prevention. *Child Abuse & Neglect, 36*(2), 156–165.

Felitti, V. J. (1991). Long-term medical consequences of incest, rape, and molestation. *Southern Medical Journal, 84*, 328–331.

Felitti, V. J., Anda, R. F., Nordenberg, D., Williamson, D. F., Spitz, A. M., Edwards, V., . . . Marks, J. S. (1998). Relationship of childhood abuse and household dysfunction to many of the leading causes of death in adults. The Adverse Childhood Experiences (ACE) Study. *American Journal of Preventive Medicine, 14*(4), 245–258. doi:S0749379798000178 [pii]

Ferguson, K. M. (2009). Exploring family environment characteristics and multiple abuse experiences among homeless youth. *Journal of Interpersonal Violence, 24*(11), 1875–1891.

Finestone, H. M., Stenn, P., Davies, F., Stalker, C., Fry, R., & Koumanis, J. (2000). Chronic pain and health care utilization in women with a history of childhood sexual abuse. *Child Abuse & Neglect, 24*, 547–556.

Gagne, M.-H., Lavoie, F., & Hebert, M. (2005). Victimization during childhood and revictimization in dating relationships in adolescent girls. *Child Abuse & Neglect, 29*, 1155–1172.

Golding, J. M. (1994). Sexual assault history and physical health in randomly selected Los Angeles women. *Health Psychology, 13*, 130–138.

Green, B. L., Kaltman, S., Frank, L., Glennie, M., Subramanian, A., Fritts-Wilson, M., . . . Chung, J. (2011). Primary care providers' experiences with trauma patients: A qualitative study. *Psychological Trauma, 3*(1), 37–41.

Heim, C., & Nemeroff, C. B. (2009). Neurobiology of posttraumatic stress disorder. *CNS Spectrums, 14*(1, Suppl. 1), 13–24.

Helgeson, V. S., & Fritz, H. L. (1998). A theory of unmitigated communion. *Personality & Social Psychology Review, 2*, 173–183.

Holzer, S. R., Uppala, S., Wonderlich, S. A., Crosby, R. D., & Simonich, H. (2008). Mediational significance of PTSD in the relationship of sexual trauma and eating disorders. *Child Abuse & Neglect, 32*, 561–566.

Hulme, P. A. (2000). Symptomatology and health care utilization of women primary care patients who experienced childhood sexual abuse. *Child Abuse & Neglect, 24*, 1471–1484.

Jenson-Campbell, L. A., & MacDonald, G. (2011). Introduction: Experiencing the ache of social injuries—an integrative approach to understanding social pain. In G. MacDonald & L. A. Jensen-Campbell (Eds.), *Social pain: Neuropsychological and health implications of loss and exclusion* (pp. 3–8). Washington, DC: American Psychological Association.

Kendall-Tackett, K. A. (2007). Cardiovascular disease and metabolic syndrome as sequelae of violence against women: A psychoneuroimmunology approach. *Trauma, Violence and Abuse, 8*, 117–126.

Kendall-Tackett, K. A. (Ed.). (2010). *The psychoneuroimmunology of chronic disease*. Washington, DC: American Psychological Association.

Kendall-Tackett, K. A. (2013). *Treating the lifetime health effects of childhood victimization* (2nd ed.). Kingston, NJ: Civic Research Institute.

Kendall-Tackett, K. A., & Eckenrode, J. (1996). The effects of neglect on academic achievement and disciplinary problems: A developmental approach. *Child Abuse & Neglect, 20*, 161–169.

Kendall-Tackett, K. A., Marshall, R., & Ness, K. E. (2000). Victimization, healthcare use and health maintenance. *Family Violence & Sexual Assault Bulletin, 16*, 18–21.

Kessler, R. C. (2012). The costs of depression. *Psychiatric Clinics of North America, 35*(1), 1–14.

Kiecolt-Glaser, J. K., Belury, M. A., Porter, K., Beversdoft, D., Lemeshow, S., & Glaser, R. (2007). Depressive symptoms, omega-6: Omega-3 fatty acids, and inflammation in older adults. *Psychosomatic Medicine, 69*, 217–224.

Kop, W. J., & Gottdiener, J. S. (2005). The role of immune system parameters in the relationship between depression and coronary artery disease. *Psychosomatic Medicine, 67*, S37–S41.

Leserman, J., & Drossman, D. A. (2007). Relationship of abuse history to functional gastrointestinal disorders and symptoms: Some possible mediating mechanisms. *Trauma, Violence, & Abuse, 8*(3), 331–343.

Lesperance, F., & Frasure-Smith, N. (2000). Depression in patients with cardiac disease: A practical review. *Journal of Psychosomatic Research, 48*, 379–391.

MacDonald, G., Borsook, T. K., & Spielmann, S. (2011). Defensive avoidance of social pain via perceptions of social threat and reward. In G. MacDonald & L. A. Jensen-Campbell (Eds.), *Social pain: Neuropsychological and health implications of loss and exclusion* (pp. 141–160). Washington, DC: American Psychological Association.

Maunder, R. G., Peladeau, N., Savage, D., & Lancee, W. J. (2010). The prevalence of childhood adversity among healthcare workers and its relationship to adult life events, distress and impairment. *Child Abuse & Neglect, 34*, 114–123.

Messman-Moore, T. L., & Brown, A. L. (2004). Child maltreatment and perceived family environment as risk factors for adult rape: Is child sexual abuse the most salient experience? *Child Abuse & Neglect, 28*, 1019–1034.

Messman-Moore, T. L., Coates, A. A., Gaffey, K. J., & Johnson, C. F. (2008). Sexuality, substance use, and susceptibility to victimization: Risk for rape and sexual coercion in a prospective study of college women. *Journal of Interpersonal Violence, 23*(12), 1730–1746.

Munroe, C. D., Kibler, J. L., Ma, M., Dollar, K. M., & Coleman, M. (2010). The relationship between posttraumatic stress symptoms and sexual risk: Examining potential mechanisms. *Psychological Trauma, 2*(1), 49–53.

National Alliance on Mental Illness. (2013). *The impact and cost of mental illness: The case of depression.* Retrieved from http://www.nami.org/Template.cfm?Section=Policymakers_Toolkit&Template=/ContentManagement/ContentDisplay.cfm&ContentID=19043

O'Leary, P., Coohey, C., & Easton, S. D. (2010). The effect of severe child sexual abuse and disclosure on mental health during adulthood. *Journal of Child Sexual Abuse, 19*, 275–289.

Persons, E., Kershaw, T., Sikkema, K. J., & Hansen, N. B. (2010). The impact of shame on health-related quality of life among HIV-positive adults with a history of childhood sexual abuse. *AIDS Patient Care & STDs, 24*(9), 571–580.

Rich-Edwards, J. W., Spiegelman, D., Hibert, E. N. L., Jun, H.-J., Todd, T. J., Kawachi, I., & Wright, R. J. (2010). Abuse in childhood and adolescence as a predictor of type-2 diabetes in adult women. *American Journal of Preventive Medicine, 39*(6), 529–536.

Robles, T. F., Glaser, R., & Kiecolt-Glaser, J. K. (2005). Out of balance: A new look at chronic stress, depression, and immunity. *Current Directions in Psychological Science, 14*, 111–115.

Sachs-Ericsson, N., Kendall-Tackett, K. A., & Hernandez, A. (2007). Childhood abuse, chronic pain, and depression in the National Comorbidity Survey. *Child Abuse & Neglect, 31*, 531–547.

Sandberg, D. A., Suess, E. A., & Heaton, J. L. (2010). Attachment anxiety as a mediator of the relationship between interpersonal trauma and posttraumatic symptomatology among college women. *Journal of Interpersonal Violence, 25*(1), 33–49.

Sareen, J., Cox, B. J., Stein, M. B., Afifi, T. O., Fleet, C., & Asmundson, G. J. (2007). Physical and mental comorbidity, disability, and suicidal behavior associated with posttraumatic stress disorder in a large community sample. *Psychosomatic Medicine, 69*(3), 242–248. doi:PSY.0b013e31803146d8 [pii] 10.1097/PSY.0b013e31803146d8

Scott, K. M., VonKorff, M., Alonso, J., Angermeyer, M. C., Benjet, C., Bruffaerts, R., . . . Posada-Villa, J. (2008). Childhood adversity, early-onset depressive/anxiety disorders, and adult-onset asthma. *Psychosomatic Medicine, 70*, 1035–1043.

Shonkoff, J. P., Boyce, W. T., & McEwen, B. S. (2009). Neuroscience, molecular biology, and the childhood roots of health disparities: Building a new framework for health promotion and disease prevention. *JAMA, 301*(21), 2252–2259. doi:301/21/2252 [pii] 10.1001/jama.2009.754

Smith, T. W. (1992). Hostility and health: Current status of a psychosomatic hypothesis. *Health Psychology, 11*, 139–150.

Steel, J. L., & Herlitz, C. A. (2005). The association between childhood and adolescent sexual abuse and proxies for sexual risk behavior: A random sample of the general population of Sweden. *Child Abuse & Neglect, 29*, 1141–1153.

Suarez, E. C. (2006). Sex differences in the relation of depressive symptoms, hostility, and anger expression to indices of glucose metabolism in nondiabetic adults. *Health Psychology, 25*, 484–492.

Suglia, S. F., Ryan, L., Laden, F., Dockery, D. W., & Wright, R. J. (2008). Violence exposure, a chronic psychosocial stressor, and childhood lung function. *Psychosomatic Medicine, 70*, 160–169.

Talbot, N. L., Chapman, B., Conwell, Y., McCollumn, K., Franus, N., Cotescu, S., & Duberstein, P. R. (2009). Childhood sexual abuse is associated with physical illness burden and functioning in psychiatric patients 50 years of age or older. *Psychosomatic Medicine, 71*, 417–422.

Teegan, F. (1999). Childhood sexual abuse and long-term sequelae. In A. Maercker, M. Schutzwohl, & Z. Solomon (Eds.), *Posttraumatic stress disorder: A lifespan developmental perspective* (pp. 97–112). Seattle, WA: Hogrefe & Huber.

Tjaden, P., & Thoennes, N. (2000). *Extent, nature, and consequences of intimate partner violence: Findings from the National Violence Against Women Survey.* Washington, DC: U.S. Department of Justice, Office of Justice Programs, National Institute of Justice.

Tucci, A. M., Kerr-Correa, F., & Souza-Formigoni, M. L. O. (2010). Childhood trauma in substance use disorder and depression: An analysis by gender among a Brazilian clinical sample. *Child Abuse & Neglect, 34,* 95–104.

Walling, S. M., Eriksson, C. B., Putman, K. M., & Foy, D. W. (2011). Community violence exposure, adverse childhood experiences, and posttraumatic distress among urban development workers. *Psychological Trauma, 3*(1), 42–49.

Wegman, H. L., & Stetler, C. (2009). A meta-analytic review of the effects of childhood abuse on medical outcomes in adulthood. *Psychosomatic Medicine, 71,* 805–812.

Wong, W. C. W., Leung, P. W. S., Tang, C. S. K., Chen, W.-Q., Lee, A., & Ling, D. C. (2009). To unfold a hidden epidemic: Prevalence of child maltreatment and its health implications among high school students in Guangzhou, China. *Child Abuse & Neglect, 33,* 441–450.

Woolf, C. J., & Salter, M. W. (2000). Neuronal plasticity: Increasing the gain in pain. *Science, 288,* 1765–1768.

Gender, Race/ Ethnicity, and Culture in Trauma Psychology

4

xposure to trauma is associated with a wide array of psychological and health consequences. A key investigation in the field of psychological trauma is whether the experience and response to trauma is similar across diverse groups of people or whether there are variations in exposure and response to trauma that call for more targeted models of assessment and clinical intervention. Differences in the trauma response may be due to biological, psychological, or sociocultural factors that confer additional risk for or protection against the development of posttraumatic stress disorder (PTSD). This chapter examines the ways in which the experience, interpretation, and response to trauma may vary by gender, race or ethnicity, and culture.

GENDER DIFFERENCES IN TRAUMA EXPOSURE AND PTSD

Findings from large-scale epidemiological surveys indicate significant gender differences in trauma exposure and PTSD. For example, the National Comorbidity Survey, a nationally representative sample of Americans, found that approximately 61% of men and 51% of women were exposed to traumatic events in their lifetimes, yet only 5% of men developed PTSD compared to 10% of women (Kessler, Sonnega, Bromet, Hughes, & Nelson, 1995), reflecting a twofold greater vulnerability among women. Likewise, Frans, Rimmo, Åberg, and Fredrikson (2005) conducted a survey of 1,784 individuals in Sweden and similarly found that while there was a greater percentage of men exposed to trauma than women (84% versus 77%), women had a greater lifetime conditional risk of PTSD than men (7.4% versus 3.6% respectively).

Situational Vulnerability

Various theories have been put forth to explain the differential gender risk for developing PTSD, including the *situational vulnerability theory* and the *female vulnerability theory*. Those adhering to the *situational vulnerability* theory (Pimlott-Kubiak & Cortina, 2003) argue that the greater rates of PTSD found among women may be due to the type or severity of trauma to which women are exposed. Despite lower rates of trauma exposure in general, women are more likely to be exposed to chronic high-impact traumas such as childhood sexual abuse and rape (Olff et al., 2007; Tolin & Foa, 2006). Indeed, estimates reveal that approximately 20% of women have been raped in their lifetime compared to only 1% of men (Black et al., 2011). Men, in contrast, are more likely to be exposed to nonsexual physical assaults, combat traumas, and accidents (Tolin & Breslau, 2007). This difference in type of trauma exposure is critical. Sexual violence is considered one of the highest risk factors for the development of PTSD. Studies show that compared to other types of traumas (e.g., physical assault or combat), rape exposure is most strongly associated with PTSD (Norris, Foster, & Weishaar, 2002).

Cortina and Kubiak (2006) evaluated these two theories by reanalyzing data from the Violence Against Women Survey (VAWS). Using a sample of 591 individuals who were victims of partner violence, Cortina and Kubiak found that on average, women had a greater risk of exposure to sexual violence across their lifetime than men. Gender was a significant independent predictor of PTSD, with women reporting more severe PTSD symptoms than men. Likewise, history of sexual violence was a significant independent predictor of PTSD. However, when both gender and history of sexual violence were included in the same prediction model, gender was no longer a significant predictor of PTSD, suggesting that it was the history of sexual violence that was driving the development of PTSD (Cortina & Kubiak, 2006). Researchers use findings like these to support the idea that exposure to more violent events, not an inherent gender vulnerability, increases the risk of posttraumatic stress.

Several theorists, however, point to studies that controlled for type of trauma exposure and found that women's risk for developing PTSD was still twofold (Olff et al., 2007; Tolin & Foa, 2006). For example, several studies of adults and children with histories of childhood sexual abuse found that women and girls were still more likely to develop PTSD (Tolin & Foa, 2006). Likewise, studies of men and women exposed to nonsexual assault have also found greater prevalence of PTSD among women, suggesting the higher vulnerability is not solely due to characteristics of the trauma (Tolin & Foa, 2006). Moreover, when potential methodological problems were controlled for, including gender differences in symptom reporting, the gender difference in PTSD persisted, suggesting it is a real issue (Chung & Breslau, 2008; Tolin & Foa, 2006).

Female Vulnerability Hypothesis

Researchers thus speculate that women may be more likely to develop PTSD because of specific psychological or biological vulnerabilities that place them at greater risk than men (Olff et al., 2007). Several studies lend support to the *female vulnerability* hypothesis. For example, studies of gender differences in cognitive appraisals or interpretations of traumatic events indicate that women are more likely than men to report appraisals of threat and loss of control in response to trauma (Olff et al., 2007). These differences in cognitive appraisals in turn may be associated with gender differences in the biological response to traumatic stress, which then contributes to greater vulnerability to developing PTSD (Rasmusson & Friedman, 2002).

Likewise, gender differences in the acute psychological and biological reactions to stress may also influence risk for PTSD. Studies indicate two types of acute stress reactions are prominent during and after exposure to trauma: emotional reactions, such as intense fear, helplessness, and horror, or dissociative reactions, such as feeling disconnected or detached from one's body or feeling as if the environment is unreal or hazy. Both types of responses are strongly associated with later development of PTSD.

Women May Experience More Acute Stress Reactions

A comprehensive review of the literature revealed that women were more likely to experience both types of acute stress reactions, which may increase their risk for PTSD (Irish et al., 2011; Olff et al., 2007). For example, Norris and colleagues (2002) found that women were more likely than men to view similar events as more threatening. Brewin, Andrews, and Rose (2000) found that women were more likely to endorse intense fear, helplessness, and horror at the time of the trauma. Higher levels of peritraumatic dissociation were also found among women compared to men (Bryant & Harvey, 2003). In contrast, men were more likely to endorse hyperarousal symptoms, which uniquely heighten their risk for PTSD. Preliminary studies also suggest women may have a more sensitive biological stress response system, which may influence the development of PTSD (Olaff et al., 2007). Taken together, these findings point to the ways in which gender differences in reactions during exposure to trauma may account for the increased risk of PTSD among women.

Posttrauma Cognitions and Coping Responses

Another area that has been examined to help explain gender differences in PTSD is posttrauma cognitions and coping responses. Research shows that women are more likely to blame themselves for the trauma happening, perceive themselves as damaged or incompetent, and view the world as unsafe (Cromer & Smyth, 2010; Tolin & Breslau, 2007). It has generally been theorized that gender role socialization processes may play a significant role in the way men and women cope in the aftermath of trauma (Christiansen & Elklit, 2012; Olaff et al., 2007). Moreover, different types of coping response may be more adaptive for women than men and lead to different pathways in the development of posttraumatic distress. Women are more likely to utilize emotion-focused coping such as seeking social support and expressing their emotions (i.e., they utilize "tend and befriend" behaviors).

Lack of or insufficient social support may then have a more detrimental effect on women than men. Women have also been found to utilize more avoidance coping strategies, such as drinking, which may serve as a form of continued dissociation. Some theorize that dissociative responses kick in when "tend and befriend" attempts are ineffective (Christiansen & Elklit, 2012). As mentioned earlier, however, dissociative responses pre- and posttrauma increase risk for PTSD and slow down the rate of recovery from posttraumatic stress.

Men, on the other hand, are more likely to display aggressive behaviors and use problem-focused coping, such as seeking practical support (some consider these behaviors "fight or flight" responses; see Christiansen & Elklit, 2012). The differential ways in which women and men implement certain combinations of coping responses may significantly influence the development or maintenance of PTSD symptoms (Olaff et al., 2007). To date, however, empirical findings in support of the link between coping responses and elevated risk for PTSD have been mixed, with no definitive pathways emerging (Christiansen & Elklit, 2012; Olaff et al., 2007; Tolin & Foa, 2006).

Gender Differences in PTSD Symptomatology

Although the literature to date points to certain gender differences in peri- or posttraumatic risk factors that may account for the heighten risk for PTSD among women, very few studies have examined whether the expression of PTSD, once diagnosed, is similar for men and women. Preliminary studies suggest men and women display similar types and levels of PTSD symptoms with comparable clinical profiles (Christiansen & Elklit, 2012).

However, one study conducted by Galovski, Mott, Young-Xu, and Resick (2011) examined a sample of 142 women and 45 men diagnosed with PTSD and found that the women reported significantly greater somatic complaints than the men. The authors hypothesized that this finding may be related to the greater injuries suffered by the women during their trauma. The men, on the other hand, reported more current feelings of anger when exposed to reminders of the trauma than the women did, confirming gender differences in trauma-related state anger. This differential expression, however, may lead to different outcomes in social support. Whereas anger may reduce the levels of social support available to men, expressions of health concerns may increase women's access to health systems and other forms of support (Christiansen & Elklit, 2012).

Gender Differences in PTSD Treatment Process and Outcome

As noted earlier, gender role socialization may influence the degree of comfort men and women feel with expressing and processing their emotional experiences (Briere & Scott, 2012). Whereas women may be more comfortable with feelings of sadness and fear, they may be less likely to experience and express feelings of anger. Women are also more likely to seek out and receive social support. The reverse may be true for men, who are more likely to experience and express anger and less likely to access and express more vulnerable feelings, such as sadness or fear.

In line with their greater fight-or-flight tendencies, men may be more cognitively focused on ways in which they can resolve their difficulties and be less likely to access and express their emotional experiences. These differences in emotional responding may have important implications for treatment process and outcome and should be taken into consideration. Empirical studies on gender differences in PTSD treatment outcomes, however, have been limited. Blain, Galovski, and Robinson (2010) conducted a comprehensive review of studies examining sex differences in PTSD treatment outcomes and found that while a majority of the studies reviewed did not detect gender differences in outcomes, a few studies did find significant differences. Women were more likely than men to benefit from trauma-focused treatment; men were more likely than women to drop out of treatment. Thus it remains unclear whether there is a significant differential effect of gender on PTSD treatment outcomes.

Summary

Research to date suggests that women are twice as likely to develop PTSD in response to a traumatic event. Gender differences in exposure to certain types of traumas (e.g., childhood sexual abuse, rape) may partly explain this difference, with women reporting greater exposure to high-impact traumas. Additional research suggests that gender differences in the psychological and biological processes activated during and after trauma exposure may also help explain the greater risk of PTSD among women. Women are more likely to experience acute trauma reactions such as intense fear, helplessness, and horror, as well as peritraumatic dissociation, than men, which may heighten their vulnerability to PTSD.

Cognitively, women are more likely to perceive the traumatic event as life-threatening and representing a loss of control compared to men. Gender differences in the biological stress response systems may also influence trauma response in men and women. These findings lend support to the idea that there might be two different pathways to PTSD for men and women. However, once diagnosed with PTSD, the expression of PTSD symptoms appears to be similar for men and women. Nevertheless, differences in peritraumatic risk factors and posttrauma coping responses should be considered during treatment preparation and implementation. Gender role socialization or expectations may determine the degree to which men and women are able to process their emotional experiences. Studies to date, however, highlight that men and women benefit equally from PTSD treatments.

RACE/ETHNICITY, TRAUMA EXPOSURE, AND PTSD

It has been generally recognized that groupings based solely on race, ethnicity, or culture have their limitations. Race as a concept has had a controversial history in terms of its meaning and its use in research. Although the term race has typically been used to classify groups of people based on biological or physical characteristics (e.g., African American or White American), it is now well known, from a biological perspective, that there are more within-group genetic differences than there are between-group genetic differences (Egede, 2006; U.S. Department of Health and Human Services, 2001).

The psychological significance of race often stems from the responses that racial group members receive from majority group members due to their skin tone or facial features. Ethnicity refers to the identification of oneself to a particular group based on a shared culture or heritage. Being a member of a racial or ethnic minority group typically involves significant experiences with racism, prejudice, and discrimination due to one's minority status. Culture refers to the norms, attitudes, values, and behaviors of a particular group that are learned and transmitted intergenerationally (Egede, 2006; U.S. Department of Health and Human Services, 2001).

Racial and ethnic minority groups (African Americans, Hispanics/Latinos, Asian Americans, etc.) constitute approximately 37% of the United States (U.S. Census Bureau, 2012), yet they are grossly underrepresented in trauma research. There is a growing body of research, however, indicating that racial and ethnic minorities may experience and respond to trauma differently than White Americans. Information on the differential exposure and effects of trauma among racial or ethnic minority groups is essential for the development and testing of targeted interventions for those at risk.

Some studies indicate that the rates of PTSD among racial and ethnic minorities are quite similar to that among White Americans, though other studies indicate the opposite is true, with racial or ethnic minorities evidencing higher rates of PTSD when compared with Whites. For example, Adams and Boscarino (2005) conducted a study of 2,368 New York City residents exposed to the World Trade Center attacks and found no racial or ethnic differences in postdisaster PTSD or PTSD symptom severity. In a nationally representative sample of 5,424 adults from the National Comorbidity Survey Replication (NCS-R) study, Breslau et al. (2006) found no significant racial or ethnic differences in risk for PTSD among Hispanics, Blacks, and Whites. Finally, Ghafoori, Barragan, Tohidian, and Palinkas (2012) found no significant racial/ethnic differences in rates of PTSD among Blacks and Whites in an urban clinical sample of 170 trauma-exposed adults.

In contrast, Perilla, Norris, and Lavizzo (2002), in a sample of 404 adult survivors of Hurricane Andrew, found that African Americans had elevated rates of PTSD compared with Caucasians. Himle et al. (2009) examined a subgroup of participants from the National Survey on American Life (NSAL) and the NCS-R and found that Blacks were more likely to meet criteria for PTSD. Dohrenwend, Turner, Turse, Lewis-Fernández, and Yager (2008) found that Hispanics and Blacks were more likely to develop and have elevated rates of PTSD after combat exposure compared to Whites.

Theories of Racial/Ethnic Disparities in PTSD

Racial/ethnic disparities in prevalence rates of PTSD have been attributed to *differential exposure* to types of traumas that confer greater risk for PTSD or to *differential vulnerability* to the effects of traumatic events after exposure (Perilla et al., 2002). Racial/ethnic minorities are more likely to be exposed to more frequent and severe stressors (e.g., chronic poverty, high-crime neighborhoods, racism, discrimination) due to their lower socioeconomic status, which may enhance their risk for development of PTSD (Hatch & Dohrenwend, 2007; Turner & Avison, 2003).

Turner and Avison (2003) conducted a survey of 899 young men and women (ages 18–22) and found that African Americans reported exposure to more stressful life events (e.g., witnessing violence, experiencing discrimination) than Whites. In a comprehensive review, Alim, Charney, and Mellman (2006) found that African Americans were more likely to be exposed to violent traumas such as homicide, physical assaults, and rape than Whites. The authors noted that the differential exposure was likely due to their residing in extremely poor urban neighborhoods, which increases risk of exposure to traumatic events (Alim et al., 2006). Hatch and Dohrenwend (2007) conducted a comprehensive review of studies from 1989 to 2005 that examined the distribution of life events (stressful and traumatic) among the population and concluded that "when racial/ethnic differences in prejudice and discrimination events are factored in, it seems reasonable to conclude that, on balance, exposure to stressful events other than the traumatic tends to be more prevalent among African-Americans and perhaps other racial/ethnic minorities than among majority whites" (p. 327).

Likewise, Roberts, Gilman, Breslau, Breslau, and Koenen (2010) examined data from 34,653 adults who completed the National Epidemiologic Survey on Alcohol and Related Conditions (NESARC) and found that Blacks and Hispanics had a higher risk of exposure to child maltreatment than Whites. Moreover, Asians, Black men, and Hispanic women were more likely to be exposed to war-related traumas than other groups. Taken together, these findings support the differential exposure theory.

However, even after adjusting for type of trauma exposure, Roberts et al. (2010) found that Blacks had a slightly higher risk of developing PTSD, and Asians a lower risk, than Whites. Likewise, Dohrenwend et al. (2008) controlled for severity of combat exposure and found that differences in risk for PTSD between Hispanics and Whites continued to persist, with Hispanics at greater risk. These findings suggest additional factors may be at play in the increased risk for PTSD among racial and ethnic minorities.

Risk Factors for Development of PTSD

Researchers have examined multiple risk factors specific to racial and ethnic minorities that may increase their vulnerability to developing PTSD after exposure to trauma, including lower socioeconomic status, increased rates of unemployment, exposure to racial prejudice and discrimination, sociocultural coping strategies, lack of access to social support, and limited mental health services utilization.

Pole, Best, Metzler, and Marmar (2005) examined the factors associated with the greater risk of PTSD among Hispanics in a convenience sample of police officers. They compared 189

Hispanics to 162 non-Hispanic Blacks and 317 non-Hispanic Whites on measures of trauma exposure, peritraumatic dissociation, posttrauma coping, and posttrauma social context (i.e., social support and perceived racism). They found that Hispanic police officers reported significantly more PTSD symptom severity than non-Hispanic Blacks and non-Hispanic Caucasians. Moreover, compared to non-Hispanic Caucasians, Hispanics reported significantly greater avoidance/numbing and hyperarousal symptoms, suggesting differential symptom expression. Hispanic officers also reported higher levels of peritraumatic dissociation at the time of the index trauma, engaged in more wishful thinking, and reported more self-blame than non-Hispanic Blacks and Caucasian officers, all of which contributed to greater risk of PTSD symptom severity. Finally, in terms of posttrauma social context, Hispanic officers reported more workplace racism and less social support than non-Hispanic Caucasians. The authors theorized that the wishful thinking might be associated with specific cultural and religious beliefs (e.g., fatalism; i.e., holding the belief that one has no control over one's destiny and thus one's recovery or future is in God's hands) that may not be adaptive in recovery from trauma (Pole et al., 2005).

Alcántara, Casement, and Lewis-Fernández (2013) further explored this issue by conducting a systematic review of peer-reviewed studies from 1991 to 2012. After controlling for methodological issues, they also found that Latinos were more likely to report peritraumatic dissociation and panic, engage in self-blame, and have a fatalistic belief system than non-Latinos, which increased their risk for PTSD.

Race-related stressors, such as racial prejudice, and stigmatization, were found to be significant predictors of PTSD diagnosis and symptom severity among African Americans and Asians (Alim et al., 2006; Loo, 2007; Pole, Gone, & Kulkarni, 2008). Chronic exposure to race-related stressors is associated with increased levels of stress and negative emotional reactions, which may make one more vulnerable to psychopathology (Pole et al., 2008). Moreover, certain discriminatory practices (e.g., hate crimes) may be traumatic events in and of themselves, which increases exposure to trauma among racial and ethnic minorities. Further studies exploring differences in posttrauma coping strategies among African Americans and Whites reveal that African Americans are more likely to utilize religion and spirituality as coping strategies. While these coping strategies may serve a protective function in many areas of their life, findings have been mixed in their ability to confer protection against the development of PTSD (Pole et al., 2008).

Socioeconomic status, often measured as a combination of educational, financial, and employment resources, has been found to be a significant predictor of PTSD and other mental health disorders in the population in general (American Psychological Association, 2013; Hatch & Dohrenwend, 2007). Studies indicate people from lower socioeconomic backgrounds are more likely to be exposed to greater and more severe violence and develop PTSD than those from middle- or upper-socioeconomic brackets (American Psychological Association, 2013; Hatch & Dohrenwend, 2007). Since racial and ethnic minorities are more likely to be members of a lower socioeconomic bracket, this increases their risk of PTSD (Alcántara et al., 2013; Pole et al., 2008).

Studies also indicate racial and ethnic minorities may be less likely to seek and receive mental health treatment, which may further compound their posttrauma recovery (Alcántara et al., 2013; Alim et al., 2006; Pole et al., 2008; Roberts et al., 2011). Moreover, once in treatment, racial and ethnic minorities may have higher dropout rates than Whites. Barriers to treatment entry and completion may include factors such as stigma, mistrust of clinicians and service providers, lack of access to evidence-based treatments, and poor quality of care.

Racial/Ethnic Differences in Treatment Process and Outcomes

Effective treatments for PTSD exist, yet very few studies have examined racial or ethnic differences in PTSD treatment outcomes. Most of the trials conducted to date have contained primarily Whites, so it remains unknown whether treatments are equally effective for racial and ethnic minorities or whether assessment or treatment strategies need to be tailored for the specific population at hand.

In one of the few trials to date, Zoellner, Feeny, Fitzgibbons, and Foa (1999) randomly assigned 95 women (60 Caucasians and 35 African Americans) with chronic PTSD to either cognitive behavioral therapy or a wait-list control condition and examined racial and ethnic differences in treatment response. Both groups demonstrated improvements in their PTSD symptomatology. Moreover, there were no significant differences in treatment response between African American and Caucasian women after receiving cognitive behavioral therapy treatments for PTSD, suggesting that the benefits of treatment cut across race and ethnicity.

Feske (2001), using a case-series design, treated 10 low-income women (eight African Americans and two Caucasians) with prolonged exposure therapy and had a 50% dropout rate. Of the five who remained in treatment (three African Americans and two Caucasians), there were clinically significant improvements in PTSD symptoms, but general anxiety and depression symptoms remained high. The author noted that the removal of structural barriers, such as transportation and child care, were essential to continued treatment participation.

Carter, Mitchell, and Sbrocco (2012) conducted a comprehensive review of the PTSD treatment outcome literature completed over the past 30 years for adults and generally concluded that racial and ethnic minority groups benefited equally when provided with PTSD treatment. The authors noted, however, that given methodological limitations with some of the studies reviewed, the lack of difference in outcomes should be taken with caution.

Summary

Research to date suggests that certain racial or ethnic minority groups may have an elevated risk for developing PTSD in response to traumatic events compared with White Americans. Racial and ethnic differences in exposure to certain types of high-impact traumas may partly explain this difference. Additionally, racial and ethnic minorities are more likely to be socially disadvantaged due to their lower socioeconomic status, which may expose them to more frequent and severe stressors (e.g., chronic poverty; high-crime neighborhoods), which may then enhance their vulnerability and risk for development of PTSD after exposure to trauma.

Moreover, factors such as exposure to racial prejudice and discrimination, sociocultural coping strategies, lack of access to social support, and limited mental health services utilization may also contribute to elevated risk of PTSD. There are few studies to date examining racial or ethnic differences in PTSD treatment response. Yet preliminary findings suggest treatment benefits cut across racial/ethnic groups. Nevertheless, clinicians and service providers should remain mindful of the different risk factors and barriers to treatment entry and retention specific to each racial or ethnic minority group.

CROSS-CULTURAL VALIDITY OF PTSD

Finally, another area that has received increased attention in trauma psychology is the question of whether the construct of PTSD has cross-cultural validity: Does the diagnosis of PTSD emerge in non-Western cultures after exposure to trauma? Some argue that the response to trauma is universal and PTSD thus should emerge in non-Western countries. Others argue that there are cross-cultural variations in response to trauma that should be acknowledged and respected when conceptualizing and treating PTSD (Marsella, 2010).

Marsella (2010), an esteemed researcher in cross-cultural trauma psychology, reviewed the history of the critiques against Western views of trauma and PTSD and highlighted the ways in which many felt the Western view of PTSD and the resultant treatment were homogeneous and did not take into consideration cultural expressions of distress and patterns of response that may not meet the diagnostic criteria. Moreover, cultural influences on treatment and healing may differ significantly from those of Western mental health professionals and may include what may be considered nontraditional or alternative methods of treatment (Marsella, 2010). Thus, problems may emerge when Western countries attempt to intervene in developing countries that are dealing with trauma.

Marsella (2010), while noting the progress made in this area, argues for the recognition of the power of cultural influences in trauma response and treatment. Hinton and Lewis-Fernández (2011) also explored this question for the fifth edition of the *Diagnostic and Statistical Manual of Mental Disorders* (*DSM-5*; American Psychiatric Association, 2013). They found evidence to support the cross-cultural validity of PTSD. Specifically, surveys show that the Western definition of PTSD is diagnosable around the world in countries such as Nigeria, China, Japan, and Mexico. However, findings also suggest that the expression of PTSD may vary cross-culturally, with some groups reporting more somatic symptoms. Moreover, the meaning of the trauma experience may vary cross-culturally. Cultural syndromes may co-occur with PTSD and influence assessment and treatment in important ways and thus should be taken into consideration (Hinton & Lewis-Fernández, 2011). Further research in this area continues to occur and is clearly warranted.

REFERENCES

Adams, R. E., & Boscarino, J. A. (2005). Differences in mental health outcomes among Whites, African Americans, and Hispanics following a community disaster. *Psychiatry, 68*(3), 250.

Alcántara, C., Casement, M. D., & Lewis-Fernández, R. (2013). Conditional risk for PTSD among Latinos: A systematic review of racial/ethnic differences and sociocultural explanations. *Clinical Psychology Review, 33*, 107–119.

Alim, T. N., Charney, D. S., & Mellman, T. A. (2006). An overview of posttraumatic stress disorder in African Americans. *Journal of Clinical Psychology, 62*(7), 801–813.

American Psychiatric Association. (2013). *Diagnostic and statistical manual of mental disorders* (5th ed.). Washington, DC: Author.

American Psychological Association. (2013). *Violence and socioeconomic status: An American Psychological Association factsheet.* Retrieved from https://www.apa.org/pi/ses/resources/publications/factsheet-violence.pdf

Black, M. C., Basile, K. C., Breiding, M. J., Smith, S. G., Walters, M. L., Merrick, M. T., & Stevens, M. R. (2011). *The National Intimate Partner and Sexual Violence Survey (NISVS): 2010 summary report.* Atlanta, GA: National Center for Injury Prevention and Control, Centers for Disease Control and Prevention.

Blain, L. M., Galovski, T. E., & Robinson, T. (2010). Gender differences in recovery from posttraumatic stress disorder: A critical review. *Aggression and Violent Behavior, 15*, 463–474.

Breslau, J., Aguilar-Gaxiola, S., Kendler, K. S., Su, M., Williams, D., & Kessler, R. C. (2006). Specifying race-ethnic differences in risk for psychiatric disorder in a USA national sample. *Psychological Medicine, 36*(1), 57–68.

Brewin, C. R., Andrews, B., & Rose, S. (2000). Fear, helplessness, and horror in posttraumatic stress disorder: Investigating *DSM-IV* criterion A2 in victims of violent crime. *Journal of Traumatic Stress, 13*(3), 499–509.

Briere, J. N., & Scott, C. (2012). *Principles of trauma therapy: A guide to symptoms, evaluation, and treatment* (2nd ed.). Washington, DC: Sage.

Bryant, R. A., & Harvey, A. G. (2003). Gender differences in the relationship between acute stress disorder and posttraumatic stress disorder following motor vehicle accidents. *Australian and New Zealand Journal of Psychiatry, 37*, 226–229.

Carter, M. M., Mitchell, F. E., & Sbrocco, T. (2012). Treating ethnic minority adults with anxiety disorders: Current status and future recommendations. *Journal of Anxiety Disorders, 26*(4), 488–501.

Christiansen, D. M., & Elklit, A. (2012). Sex differences in PTSD. In A. Lazinica & E. Ovuga (Eds.), *Post traumatic stress disorders in a global context* (pp. 113–142). Rijeka, Croatia: InTech—Open Access Publisher.

Chung, H., & Breslau, N. (2008). The latent structure of post-traumatic stress disorder: Test of invariance by gender and trauma type. *Psychological Medicine, 38*, 563–573.

Cortina, L. M., & Kubiak, S. P. (2006). Gender and posttraumatic stress: Sexual violence as an explanation for women's increased risk. *Journal of Abnormal Psychology, 115*(4), 753–759.

Cromer, L. D., & Smyth, J. M. (2010). Making meaning of trauma: Trauma exposure doesn't tell the whole story. *Journal of Contemporary Psychotherapy, 40*, 65–72.

Egede, L. E. (2006). Race, ethnicity, culture, and disparities in health care. *Journal of General Internal Medicine, 21*(6), 667–669.

Feske, U. (2001). Treating low-income and African-American women with posttraumatic stress disorder: A case series. *Behavior Therapy, 32*(3), 585–601.

Frans, O., Rimmo, P.-A., Åberg, L., & Fredrikson, M. (2005). Trauma exposure and post-traumatic stress disorder in the general population. *Acta Psychiatrica Scandinavica, 111*, 291–299.

Galovski, T. E., Mott, J., Young-Xu, Y., & Resick, P. A. (2011). Gender differences in the clinical presentation of PTSD and its concomitants in survivors of interpersonal assault. *Journal of Interpersonal Violence, 26*(4), 789–806.

Ghafoori, B., Barragan, B., Tohidian, N., & Palinkas, L. (2012). Racial and ethnic differences in symptom severity of PTSD, GAD, and depression in trauma-exposed, urban, treatment-seeking adults. *Journal of Traumatic Stress, 25*(1), 106–110.

Hatch, S. L., & Dohrenwend, B. P. (2007). Distribution of traumatic and other stressful life events by race/ethnicity, gender, SES and age: A review of the research. *American Journal of Community Psychology, 40*(3–4), 313–332.

Himle, J. A., Baser, R. E., Taylor, R. J., Campbell, R. D., & Jackson, J. S. (2009). Anxiety disorders among African Americans, blacks of Caribbean descent, and non-Hispanic whites in the United States. *Journal of Anxiety Disorders, 23*(5), 578–590.

Hinton, D. E., & Lewis-Fernández, R. (2011). The cross-cultural validity of posttraumatic stress disorder: Implications for *DSM-5*. *Depression and Anxiety, 28*(9), 783–801.

Irish, L. A., Fischer, B., Fallon, W., Spoonster, E., Sledjeski, E. D., & Delahantya, D. L. (2011). Gender differences in PTSD symptoms:

An exploration of peritraumatic mechanisms. *Journal of Anxiety Disorders, 25*, 209–216.

Kessler, R., Sonnega, A., Bromet, E., Hughes, M., & Nelson, C. (1995). Posttraumatic stress disorder in the National Comorbidity Survey. *Archives of General Psychiatry, 52*, 1048–1060.

Loo, C. M. (2007). *PTSD among ethnic minority veterans: A National Center for PTSD fact sheet*. Retrieved from http://www.ptsd.va.gov/professional/treatment/cultural/ptsd-minority-vets.asp

Marsella, A. J. (2010). Ethnocultural aspects of PTSD: An overview of concepts, issues, and treatments. *Traumatology, 16*(4), 17–26.

Norris, F. H., Foster, J. D., & Weishaar, D. L. (2002). The epidemiology of sex differences in PTSD across developmental, societal, and research contexts. In R. Kimerling, P. Ouimette, & J. Wofle (Eds.), *Gender and PTSD* (pp. 3–42). New York, NY: The Guilford Press.

Olff, M., Langeland, W., Draijer, N., & Gersons, B. P. (2007). Gender differences in posttraumatic stress disorder. *Psychological Bulletin, 133*(2), 183.

Perilla, J. L., Norris, F. H., & Lavizzo, E. A. (2002). Ethnicity, culture, and disaster response: Identifying and explaining ethnic differences in PTSD six months after Hurricane Andrew. *Journal of Social and Clinical Psychology, 21*(1), 20–45.

Pimlott-Kubiak, S., & Cortina, L. (2003). Gender, victimization, and outcomes: Reconceptualizing risk. *Journal of Consulting and Clinical Psychology, 71*, 528–539.

Pole, N., Best, S. R., Metzler, T., & Marmar, C. R. (2005). Why are Hispanics at greater risk for PTSD? *Cultural Diversity and Ethnic Minority Psychology, 11*(2), 144.

Pole, N., Gone, J. P., & Kulkarni, M. (2008). Posttraumatic stress disorder among ethnoracial minorities in the United States. *Clinical Psychology: Science and Practice, 15*(1), 35–61.

Rasmusson, A. M., & Friedman, M. J. (2002). Gender issues in the neurobiology of PTSD. In R. Kimerling, P. C. Ouimette, & J. Wolfe (Eds.), *Gender and PTSD* (pp. 43–75). New York, NY: Guilford Press.

Roberts, A. L., Gilman, S. E., Breslau, J., Breslau, N., & Koenen, K. C. (2011). Race/ethnic differences in exposure to traumatic events, development of post-traumatic stress disorder, and treatment-seeking for post-traumatic stress disorder in the United States. *Psychological Medicine, 41*(1), 71–83.

Tolin, D. F., & Breslau, N. (2007). Sex differences in risk of PTSD. *The National Center for Post-Traumatic Stress Disorder PTSD Research Quarterly, 18,* 2. Retrieved from http://www.ptsd.va.gov/professional/newsletters/research-quarterly/V18N2.pdf

Tolin, D. F., & Foa, E. B. (2006). Sex differences in trauma and post-traumatic stress disorder: A quantitative review of 25 years of research. *Psychological Bulletin, 132*(6), 959–992.

Turner, R. J., & Avison, W. R. (2003). Status variations in stress exposure: Implications for the interpretation of research on race, socioeconomic status, and gender. *Journal of Health and Social Behavior, 22*(4), 488–505.

U.S. Census Bureau. (2012). *USA Statistics in Brief—Race and Hispanic Origin.* Retrieved from http://www.census.gov/compendia/statab/2012/files/racehisp.html

U.S. Department of Health and Human Services. (2001). *Mental health: Culture, race, and ethnicity—A supplement to mental health: A report of the Surgeon General.* Rockville, MD: U.S. Department of Health and Human Services, Substance Abuse and Mental Health Services Administration, Center for Mental Health Services. Retrieved from http://www.ncbi.nlm.nih.gov/books/NBK44243

Zoellner, L. A., Feeny, N. C., Fitzgibbons, L. A., & Foa, E. B. (1999). Response of African American and Caucasian women to cognitive behavioral therapy for PTSD. *Behavior Therapy, 30,* 581–595.

Collateral Damage: The Effects of Posttraumatic Stress Disorder on Family Members

Family members may feel hurt, alienated, or discouraged because your loved one has not been able to overcome the effects of the trauma. Family members frequently devote themselves totally to those they care for and, in the process, neglect their own needs.

—National Center for PTSD, 2010

When one member of a family suffers, it affects the entire family. They may not have experienced the traumatic event, but they live—every day—with the consequences. They are collateral damage. The challenges are ongoing, and can seem overwhelming (Link & Palinkas, 2013). Posttraumatic stress disorder (PTSD) can affect all members of a survivor's family: parents, spouses, and children. Divorce is twice as common in families with PTSD. Spouses are at increased risk for domestic violence. People with PTSD are easily startled; they have nightmares, which can interfere with their family members' sleep; and they can't handle many social situations, often isolating their families from contact with the outside world (National Center for PTSD, 2010).

PTSD can also significantly alter the personality, making an individual seem like a different person. The partner may no longer see the traits that he or she fell in love with (National Center for PTSD, 2010). Lyndsay Glenn describes herself as the home front's walking wounded of the war: She struggles to care for her 2-year-old daughter and her husband, a Marine who served two tours in Iraq and who now suffers from PTSD. In a recent interview, she said, "Sometimes I don't feel like my vows cover this horror" (Albrecht, 2013). In an interview, she describes having to give up her career to drive her husband to his appointments because traffic triggers road rage in him. At first, when he came home, the family never left the house. He was in denial about his symptoms, and he often said things to her that were hurtful. She never has time for herself. They can't go out to eat without planning for times when the restaurant is not crowded—and he has to have a corner table. They can never just "wing it" (Albrecht, 2013).

Sharon Edwards described her experiences after her husband returned from Bosnia as "living with Dr. Jekyll and Mr. Hyde." He had nightmares and extreme mood swings. His nightmares were such that they couldn't sleep in the same room. She'd go in when she heard him screaming. He'd be up half the night, and she was up caring for him, trying to calm him down. "When's it all going to get better? I don't see an end to this rainbow. It's always something else" (Albrecht, 2013).

The caregiver stress associated with a partner with PTSD has been likened to that of caring for someone with Alzheimer's or chronic schizophrenia. In one study of soldiers in Israel, caregiver burden was more associated with partner distress from PTSD than level of physical impairment in the veteran (Link & Palinkas, 2013). Caring for someone with PTSD even affects the caregiver's health. Caregivers are more likely to experience physical and mental health problems, including heart disease, hypertension, sleep problems, and depression (Albrecht, 2013).

The effect of trauma on the family can be severe and long-lasting and can ultimately lead to major problems, including family violence, substance abuse, and divorce (Carlson & Ruzek, 2007). Soldiers are, in some ways, the most visible sufferers from PTSD. High percentages of veterans return home with physical injuries, traumatic brain injuries, and PTSD. But they are not the only ones. According to the National Center for PTSD (n.d.), 50% of women and 61% of men will be exposed to at least one traumatic event in their lifetimes. Eight percent of men and 20% of women will develop PTSD. PTSD could be due to combat exposure, surviving war or genocide, rape, childhood abuse, or other traumatic experience. The problems are real and can be passed from generation to generation.

EFFECTS OF PTSD ON PARTNERS

Partners are affected by their loved ones' PTSD. PTSD can cause irritability, lack of ability to concentrate, nightmares, and fear of ordinary life situations or events, such as crowded restaurants or loud noises. Partners may be short-tempered, verbally aggressive, and very difficult to live with. Nightmares in one partner may mean that his or her partner does not sleep. The partner with PTSD may also be so impaired that he or she cannot work and does not help with household chores or caring for children. The nonimpaired spouse may feel that his or her needs are never met by his or her emotionally unavailable spouse.

Sharon Vasil describes her 4-decade struggle with PTSD after her husband Hank returned from Vietnam. He went from being "a gentle giant" to someone with a "hair-trigger temper." She'd say something she thought was innocent and they'd end up having a big argument. He'd drink a lot. They were ostracized in their neighborhood because her husband was the "crazy Vietnam vet." They were isolated. At the time, there were no support groups. She didn't have girlfriends. Her kids were not allowed to participate in outside activities. But she decided that the worst thing a wife could say was, "You're home now. Get over it and get on with your life." So they decided to fight the fight together. It was a life-altering event, and "we'll deal with it until the day we die" (Albrecht, 2013).

According to the National Center for PTSD, PTSD affects the patient's partner, including by severe and pervasive effects on marital adjustment, functioning, and mental and physical health (Price & Stevens, 2009). Some other negative effects include family violence, sexual problems, aggression, caregiver burden, and compromised parenting. Not surprisingly, divorce rates are high. In one study of Vietnam veterans, approximately 38% of marriages failed within 6 months of their return from their tour of duty (President's Commission on Mental Health, 1978). And veterans with PTSD were twice as likely to get divorced as veterans without PTSD (Kulka et al., 1990).

There are several specific ways that PTSD can affect a marriage or partnership. Following are some of the issues that researchers have found can have a negative impact on the marriage of trauma survivors.

Effects on Intimacy

The person with PTSD may dramatically change in the wake of the traumatic event. They may withdraw from others in the family (Carlson & Ruzek, 2007). The numbing and avoidance symptoms have the strongest association with relationship satisfaction (Link & Palinkas, 2013). The person with PTSD may be moody and difficult to live with but refuse to talk about what is bothering him or her (Price & Stevens, 2009). He or she may be disconnected from his or her spouse, acting as if the two are strangers.

Their sexual relationship may also be affected, further contributing to the lack of intimacy and satisfaction in the relationship.

The partner with PTSD may want to avoid social situations and may ask his or her husband or wife to stay home as well, isolating the entire family from others. He or she may be fearful of going out and may become fearful if his or her spouse goes out as well. The partner without PTSD may feel guilty for not being able to meet the needs of his or her partner or may feel angry about his or her partner's irritability or violence (National Center for PTSD, 2010).

According to the National Center for PTSD (2007b), male veterans with PTSD are significantly more likely to experience marital problems, difficulties in parenting, and overall poorer family functioning than male veterans without PTSD. Although the majority of research has been done with male veterans, a similar pattern is emerging among women veterans with PTSD. Veterans with PTSD reported less involvement, cohesion, expressiveness, self-disclosure, and consensus with partners, as well as higher levels of conflict, hostility, and physical aggression with partners (Link & Palinkas, 2013). Among men with military-related PTSD, their partners report numerous problems and generally poor family functions (Monson, Taft, & Fredman, 2009). Male partners are less likely to self-disclose and be emotionally expressive. They also have more anxiety related to relationship intimacy.

Veterans with PTSD can also have difficulties establishing and maintaining long-term relationships (Link & Palinkas, 2013). In one recent study, family and life stress during deployment was the strongest predictor of PTSD following combat exposure (Shea, Reddy, Tyrka, & Sevin, 2013). Another study of soon-to-be-deployed soldiers and their partners found higher rates of depression, PTSD symptoms, and social impairments in the partners. The soldiers had higher rates of alcohol abuse (Erbes, Meis, Polusny, & Arbisi, 2012). Consistent with previous studies, there was a reciprocal relationship between soldiers' and partners' levels of distress: The higher the soldiers' level of distress, the higher their partners'. Another study of 242 veterans and their partners found that partner substance abuse was a better predictor of veterans' substance abuse than PTSD alone (Miller, Reardon, Wolf, Prince, & Hein, 2013). These findings underscore the need for including partners in treatment for PTSD with comorbid substance abuse.

A recent study of veterans from Bosnia and Herzegovina compared 154 war veterans with PTSD, along with their wives, with 77 veterans without PTSD and their wives (Klaric et al., 2011). They found that veterans' PTSD was related to significantly lower levels of marital adjustment in their wives. Marital adjustment was lower still when both partners had PTSD. Husbands' avoidance symptoms best explained their wives' marital adjustment. Avoidance symptoms include veterans' inhibited intimacy and expressiveness, limited emotional expression, and lack of interest in social activities. Problems with family cohesion and lack of sexual intimacy contributed to marital discord.

Increased Partner Violence

People with PTSD are also at increased risk for partner violence (Monson et al., 2009). The hyperarousal symptoms are especially related to aggressive behavior and abuse in relationships (Link & Palinkas, 2013). But re-experiencing, avoidance, and hyperarousal have all been associated with verbal partner violence (Link & Palinkas, 2013). Other common comorbid disorders, such as substance abuse and depression, further exacerbate the problem (Monson et al., 2009). Male partners with PTSD are more likely to perpetrate physical aggression against their partners and children, with rates of aggression as high as 63% in the past year (Monson et al., 2009). The veterans in this study were also more likely to have major depression, substance use and dependence, and war zone atrocity exposure.

A study of 2,157 members of the Canadian Armed Forces found that perpetration rates of physical and/or sexual partner violence was 9%, with a 15% victimization rate (Zamorski & Wiens-Kinkaid, 2013). Depression was associated with both partner violence perpetration and victimization. PTSD was associated with a thrice-increased risk of partner violence perpetration. Interestingly, the risk of partner violence was lowest in those who had recent deployment. Mental disorders, high-risk drinking, relationship dissatisfaction, and remote deployment were all independently associated with abuse outcomes. The less serious types of partner violence were the most common—but even they are not trivial. These included threatening with a fist, pushing, grabbing, or shoving; slapping; putting the partner down and name calling; jealousy about communication with the opposite sex; and demanding to know the "who and where" of the partner at all times.

Unfortunately, physical and verbal aggression are also common. In one study of Vietnam veterans, 42% had been physically violent against their partner at least once in the previous year, and 92% had been verbally aggressive (Byrne & Riggs, 1996). Substance use complicates the picture when examining the relationship between PTSD, physical or psychological IPV, and the marital relationship. PTSD symptoms contributed to perpetration of intimate partner violence (IPV) because of anger and poor relationship adjustment.

A study of women's perpetration of IPV found the strongest relationship between IPV perpetration and IPV victimization (Hellmuth, Jaquier, Young-Wolff, & Sullivan, 2013). The sample was 146 low-income women, predominantly African American. Psychological IPV was by far the most common type: shouting at the partner or calling the partner names or calling him fat or ugly. Severity of PTSD re-experiencing and numbing symptoms were both related to use of IPV. However, this relationship was indirect, through alcohol abuse. The authors hypothesized using alcohol to self-medicate contributed to perpetration of IPV among women.

Secondary Posttraumatic Stress in Partners

Partners can also develop PTSD or secondary posttraumatic stress, which further complicates the situation in the family. According to the National Center for PTSD (2007b), spouses of veterans with PTSD reported lower levels of happiness, less satisfaction in their lives, and more demoralization. Almost half described themselves as "on the verge of a nervous breakdown." Not surprisingly, caregivers of family members with PTSD experience more physical and mental stress than those whose partners do not have PTSD. The caregivers have more depression, anxiety, and dysphoria. The more symptoms the partner with PTSD had, the more intense the symptoms in the spouse (Price & Stevens, 2009). Spouses can also develop secondary posttraumatic stress simply by living with a partner with PTSD (National Center for PTSD, 2007b).

In a recent study of 190 civilian wives of male service members, rates of partner posttraumatic symptoms were high (Renshaw & Caska, 2012): 24% met criteria for PTSD, and 41% had significant posttraumatic stress. The authors found that 22% to 42% had PTSD, depending on the cut-off used on the scale to measure symptoms. One question the researchers sought to address was whether wives attributed their PTSD to their husbands' experiences. Of the 170 wives with symptoms, 106 (62%) indicated that their symptoms were completely unrelated to their husbands' military experience. Regardless of the severity of their husbands' symptoms, most wives attributed their symptoms to events other than their husbands' military experiences.

Unhelpful Reactions From Family Members

Carlson and Ruzek (2007) described some reactions family members might have in response to PTSD. While understandable, these reactions are ultimately not helpful for either the trauma survivor or the family.

1. **Sympathy.** It is natural to feel sorry for someone who has experienced a severe traumatic event. But this reaction becomes unhealthy when it "babies" the individual, implying that he or she is not capable of overcoming the trauma.
2. **Depression.** Depression is another common response that family members might feel in the wake of trauma

experienced by a loved one. Unfortunately, depression in a family member shatters the trauma survivor's assumptions that his or her family is a safe and predictable place. Depression might also be the result of trauma's effects on the family's change in financial circumstance. For example, following a traumatic event, the traumatized person may no longer be able to hold down a job, resulting in a significant change in the family's financial circumstances. Depression in family members might also be due to the trauma survivor's withdrawal from members of his or her family to the extent that they don't feel loved any more.

3. **Fear and worry.** If one member of the family experiences a traumatic event, the rest of the family may feel unsafe. They may take steps to ensure safety, such as installing an alarm system, getting a guard dog, or purchasing a firearm. Family members might also be afraid because of the trauma survivor's angry outbursts, violence, or reckless or self-destructive behavior. Their family member may have become a danger to himself or herself or to others.

4. **Avoidance.** Family members may avoid talking about the trauma and the problems related to it, even with close friends. They may worry about violating their loved one's privacy. Or they may fear that others will judge them or won't understand. Avoidance is especially likely if there is "shame" around the event, such as in the case of rape. The entire family may also avoid things that the trauma survivor cannot tolerate, such as public outings. Children might not understand why they can't do the things that "normal" families do and may become resentful. Spouses might also become resentful and resent being socially isolated.

5. **Guilt and shame.** Family members might also feel guilt and shame following a traumatic event, especially if they feel that they were somehow responsible for the trauma, even if their beliefs are unrealistic. They may feel guilt and shame if, somehow, they "failed to protect" their family member or

if their negligent action, however tangentially, was to blame for the traumatic event. Family members may later learn more about PTSD and feel guilty for not understanding and being supportive at the time.

6. **Anger.** Anger is another common reaction of family members after trauma. They may be angry at the person responsible. They may be angry at God for allowing it to happen. Or they may be angry at their traumatized family member when they can't "just get over it." They may also be angry at the way they are being treated, or they may resent shouldering most of the responsibility around the house. Their financial circumstances may have changed or the survivor may often be angry and irritable with them.

7. **Negative feelings.** Family members may also have strongly negative feelings about each other after the traumatic event. For example, a husband may have negative feelings about his wife after she has been raped and wonder whether there wasn't "more she could have done to resist the assault." A wife may be disgusted with the way her husband handled the traumatic event and think that he wasn't "brave" in that situation. These negative feelings, even if the person having them knows they are unfair, can have a dramatic effect on the way that family members act toward each other.

8. **Substance abuse.** All members of a family may start abusing substances as a way to cope following traumatic events. Unfortunately, this method of coping tends to only exacerbate problems.

9. **Sleep problems.** Trauma survivors' sleep may be severely compromised. They may have problems going to sleep, be restless at night, have frequent nightmares, and be up several times during night. These kinds of disruptive sleep problems can affect the sleep of the entire family, making it difficult for members to cope with the aftermath of PTSD.

CHILDREN OF TRAUMA SURVIVORS: INTERGENERATIONAL TRANSMISSION OF TRAUMA

Children can also be affected by the trauma their parents have experienced. Some common types of parenting problems include angry outbursts; physically, emotionally, and verbally abusive behavior; and withdrawal. Christal Presley indicated that her father, a Vietnam vet, "vacillated between depression and rage":

> He was hypersensitive when it came to sounds or lights, particularly sounds. I was pretty clumsy as a child, like a lot of children, and I would occasionally drop or spill things. Hearing any sound like that would make him go into war mode. He would drop on the floor, or he would come after me. (Roan, 2013)

A Department of Veterans Affairs and Department of Defense (2010) report found that children of parents with PTSD had more anxiety, emotional problems, depression, and withdrawal. Such children may be afraid of their parents and so may withdraw or act up more. Children of Operation Enduring Freedom (OEF), Operation Iraqi Freedom (OIF), and Operation New Dawn (OND) veterans with PTSD had more child depression, internalizing behaviors, and externalizing behaviors at ages 6 to 12. These children were also more likely to be afraid of the veteran (Link & Palinkas, 2013). In a study of Vietnam veterans, numbing (a specific type of avoidance symptom) was associated with every type of dysfunction in the veterans' relationships with their children (Link & Palinkas, 2013).

Psychotherapist Jim May (May, 2013) described his experience growing up with a father, a highly decorated World War II veteran, who never spoke about the war. Neither May nor his mother knew much about what his father had done during World War II. His father had nightmares that woke up the whole family, and he flew into frequent rages directed against his wife and son. His son now recognizes that his father had untreated PTSD and that he viewed his son as "the enemy." After his mother died, when May was 20 years old, he saw his father only rarely for the rest of his father's life. May described their relationship as "difficult and painful," indicating that he deeply regrets that he never was able to have a relationship with his father and that he feels that their relationship was just one more casualty of the war.

A recent review indicated that parental PTSD does not necessarily lead to child PTSD or behavior problems (Monson et al., 2009). However, another review, citing literature from the Vietnam era, found that some studies indicated that children of Vietnam veterans did show an increase in behavioral problems and higher levels of depression and that they also had a less favorable attitude toward their fathers, more apprehension and anxiety, and lower levels of creativity (Link & Palinkas, 2013).

Impaired Parenting

PTSD in parents leads to difficulties in children because it frequently impairs parenting. Children of parents with PTSD often describe damaged, preoccupied parents who are emotionally limited (Portney, 2003). Symptoms in parents, such as traumatic reliving, emotional numbing, and dissociation, do not help a child develop a reasonable sense of safety and predictability in the world. These parents are also less able to respond appropriately during their children's usual developmental crises. Parents with PTSD also have difficulties modeling a healthy sense of identity and autonomy, appropriate affect regulation, and how to maintain a balanced perspective when life challenges arise. Instead, these parents are more likely to model catastrophic, or inappropriately numbed and disassociated, responses. Therefore, the parent's high levels of anxiety can significantly interfere with the child's developmental progress.

Nikki describes the effects of both her mother's and father's PTSD on the way they parented her:

My mother, who grew up being sexually, emotionally and physically abused, did not want to become pregnant. But there I was, conceived 1 month after my parent's wedding. She was 21 years old, stuck at home with a newborn in a strange new town, a city girl without transportation, without friends, and a husband away all day at work.

My father grew up in a respectable Jewish family, taught to be nice and kind. At 18, he went to Europe in Patton's army and, to this day, cannot talk about the horrors he witnessed. He came home with undiagnosed PTSD, alcohol dependency, and a free education courtesy of the GI Bill.

I have spent most of my adult life recovering from the impact of the neglect and abuse (sexual, emotional, and physical) that my parents perpetrated on me. The silver lining to the F5 tornado of my early life is a lifelong dedication to supporting attachment parenting, good birth, breastfeeding, and the maternal–infant relationship. I am blessed, too, in that I was able to break the ancestral pattern of child abuse.

Parents with PTSD may be disengaged from their children, and when they do engage, they are sometimes abusive. In a study of 240 children and parents in Gaza, Palestine, researchers studied children's experiences of war trauma, psychological maltreatment, attachment security, posttraumatic stress, depression, and aggression (Palosaari, Punamaki, Qouta, & Diab, 2013). The authors used structural equation modeling to test the hypothesis of intergenerational transmission of trauma. They found that the fathers' war trauma was related to insecure attachment and increased the risk of mental health problems in their children. The fathers' war trauma was also related to psychological maltreatment of their children. The mothers' war trauma was not related to psychological maltreatment of their children, insecure attachment, or depression in their children. The authors concluded that fathers' war exposure should be considered a risk factor for child maltreatment.

The Effects of Trauma on Early Attachment

PTSD may have negative effects on attachment in infancy, which can affect parenting long term (Enlow, Egeland, Carlson, Blood, & Wright, 2013). One study of 566 pregnant women found that posttraumatic stress symptoms in pregnancy were associated with postpartum depression (Seng et al., 2013). And postpartum depression, alone or with comorbid PTSD, was associated with impaired bonding. The sample included three cohorts of women: PTSD-positive; trauma exposed, resilient; and nontrauma exposed. The authors concluded that women with a history of child maltreatment are at high risk for PTSD and major depressive disorder postpartum, which impairs mother–infant bonding because it affects the way mothers interact with their babies. There are well-documented long-term effects of maternal depression on infants and children. The long-term effects of maternal PTSD on are less well known, but we can speculate on those since PTSD is highly comorbid with depression. These children are themselves at risk for pathology and trauma. The authors recommended that women with a history of child maltreatment be identified as soon as possible so that they can receive appropriate treatment, preferably before pregnancy. The authors also recommend interventions that address the quality of the mother–child relationship that may be affected by PTSD.

Hairston and colleagues (2011) investigated one possible mechanism by which pregnant women with PTSD could transmit their symptoms to their offspring: infant sleep. The study included 184 first-time mothers, 83 of whom had a history of childhood abuse and PTSD, 38 mothers with a history of childhood abuse and no PTSD, and 63 control women who had no history of childhood abuse and no PTSD. They found that infants of mothers with PTSD had more sleep problems and more separation anxiety around bedtime than the other two groups. The more symptoms the mothers had, the greater the number of sleep disturbances the babies had. Infant sleep problems contributed to impaired bonding. Babies who experienced impaired mother–infant bonding at 4 months had more behavior problems at 18 months.

In another study, 97 mothers with a history of child maltreatment were compared with 53 mothers with no history of abuse on bonding with their infants at 6 weeks, 4 months, and 6 months postpartum (Muzik et al., 2013). Over the study period, all mothers increased their bonding with their infants. But the mothers with histories of abuse and of depression and PTSD postpartum had impaired measures of bonding at every assessment point. The authors stress the need for early detection and treatment of postpartum depression and PTSD as a way to prevent relationship disturbances between mother and child.

A study using two samples with prospective data sought to understand how PTSD affected the mother–infant attachment and whether this insecure attachment affected later risk for the offsprings' developing PTSD when exposed to a subsequent stressor (Enlow et al., 2013). The first sample included low-income racial or ethnic minority mothers. In this analysis, mothers' PTSD symptoms at 6 months were associated with infants' insecure attachment at 13 months. The second study was a birth cohort study ($N = 96$ mother–infant dyads). The researchers found that insecure attachment in infancy increased risk of PTSD by age 17. It was a dose–response effect, with the highest risk of symptoms associated with PTSD in adolescence. The authors concluded that promoting secure attachments in children would prevent PTSD in populations that are at high risk for trauma exposure.

Another recent study found that maternal PTSD affected infant emotional reactivity and emotion regulation (Enlow et al., 2011). Emotional regulation underlies mental health and competent functioning throughout the life span. Mothers of babies with PTSD are often impaired in their ability to regulate their emotions. One hypothesis for why this might happen is changes' in the in utero environment for mothers with PTSD making the infants more hypersensitive to stimuli and unable to calm on their own. Another possible mechanism has to do with how PTSD affects maternal interaction with their babies. This study included 52 mother–infant dyads during the first year of life. The mothers were primarily low-income and ethnic or racial minorities.

At 6 months old, the infants participated in the still face paradigm (Enlow et al., 2011). In this paradigm, the mother maintains a still face and does not respond to the infant's cues for a period of time. This is stressful for the infant, because he or she uses the mother's cues to help him or her maintain an organized social and affective state. When the mother does not respond, the infant loses the ability to regulate his or her emotions. The still face paradigm measures the infant's emotional reactivity to a stress and the ability of the mother–infant dyad to recover and regulate infant emotion following cessation of the stressor.

At 13 months, infant behavioral and emotional symptoms were assessed (Enlow et al., 2011). Infants of mothers with PTSD had difficulties with emotional regulation, both as measured in their recovery from distress following the still face and in daily life. Regulation refers to the ability to modify the intensity and duration of physiological arousal, attention, and affective state. This allows the infant to not become overwhelmed and to modulate emotions and participate in complex social interactions. Infants of PTSD-positive mothers had more internalizing, externalizing, and dysregulation at 13 months. The authors concluded that these reactions increase the infants of the PTSD-positive mothers' risk for later pathology.

Breaking the Cycle

Although the risk of child maltreatment in mothers with PTSD is high, it is not inevitable. Most mothers with abuse histories do not abuse their children. When considering breaking the cycle of abuse, factors that are important include having at least one stable relationship during childhood, participating in therapy at some point, and having a secure stable relationship with an adult partner (Egeland, Jacobvitz, & Sroufe, 1988).

Interesting, breastfeeding also appears to have a role in preventing maternal-perpetrated child maltreatment. In a 15-year longitudinal study of more than 7,000 mother–infant dyads, mothers who were not breastfeeding were more than twice as likely to physically abuse their children and 3.8 times more likely to neglect them (Strathearn, Mamun, Najman, & O'Callaghan, 2009). In addition, in a sample of 994 sexual assault survivors, exclusive breastfeeding improved the mothers' sleep as measured by multiple parameters (e.g., time to get to sleep, total sleep time, daily energy), decreased their anger and irritability, and lowered their depression risk (Kendall-Tackett, Cong, & Hale, 2013). These effects are likely due to breastfeeding's ability to downregulate the stress system and increase the presence of oxytocin, the hormone associated with love and attachment (Groer, Davis, & Hemphill, 2002; Kendall-Tackett, 2007).

Nikki describes how her decisions to mother differently, go to therapy, have a natural birth, and breastfeed her baby helped her break the cycle of abuse:

> When I was 9, I made a vow that I would never treat my kids the way my parents, especially my mother, treated me. I always remembered that. . . .
>
> Interestingly enough, it was my mother that brought me a key to healing. She always knew that there was something wrong, even though she was unable to treat me well. She was a searcher for relief from pain, and I picked up on that from her and started therapy at age 27 . . . where I continue.
>
> My mother didn't want to spend any money on my college education; I got a scholarship to college to be a nurse. Fortunately, I took to nursing. That education opened my mind to things that supported my drive to heal.
>
> I am a child of the late 1960s and 1970s: question authority, rebellion, hippies, and all that. I read *Immaculate Deception* when I was pregnant, and that fueled my desire to be a better mother. I knew that I would breastfeed and could not have told anyone why. I had the first unmedicated, Lamaze birth in the hospital. I fell in love with my baby and let my heart guide my parenting: I ended up sleeping with her, too. She was my first big teacher; on the delivery room table, I realized that my insanity would become her reality, and that motivated me to let my first marriage to the abusive physician go and to start therapy. I was driven to be better than my mother was to me.

Intergenerational Transmission of Trauma

Unfortunately, without intervention, transmission of trauma may be multigenerational. A study of grandchildren of Holocaust survivors compared 124 grandchildren whose grandparents survived the Holocaust with 124 grandchildren of grandparents who did not go through the Holocaust (Iliceto et al., 2011). They found no differences in hopelessness, dysthymia, anxiety, and self-perception. The grandchild of Holocaust survivors were well integrated into society and had middle-to-high incomes. However, their perceptions of others were highly judgmental and critical. Grandchildren of Holocaust survivors were more likely to view others as rejecting, hostile, submissive, insecure, unreliable, and competitive in interpersonal relationships. They were more irritable and angry than the controls, and their perception of life was deeply negative.

Cultural trauma is another way that traumatic events can be passed within a community. A study of the effects of the Armenian genocide of 1914 to 1918 found that 36% of a sample of 689 people of Armenian origin living in Greece or Cypress showed signs of subclinical trauma (Karenian, Livaditis, Karenian, Zafiriadis, & Bochtsou, 2011). This event took place long before most of the participants in the study were born. Nevertheless, many were affected, at least on a subclinical level. Women, older people, those who lost relatives, and those with strong ties to the Armenian community were the most vulnerable to these symptoms. These symptoms included vengeful thoughts, permanent distress, fears, shame, helplessness, and guilt. Most reported that these symptoms were present throughout their lives.

HOW FAMILIES CAN COPE WITH PTSD

When a family member has PTSD, the road is often difficult, and the demands of caregiving can be overwhelming. However, there are some resources available to help families cope. The National

Center for PTSD specifically recommends that partners of trauma survivors first seek out information so that they can better understand PTSD. Treatment for the families can include psychoeducation for family members, support groups for survivors and their partners, individual treatment, and possibly couples therapy (Price & Stevens, 2009).

The psychoeducation approach includes educating trauma survivors and their families about both trauma and PTSD, as well as suggesting possible coping strategies. There is a strong self-help component in these approaches. Price and Stevens (2009) further emphasize that relationship difficulties and social and emotional struggles are common when living with someone with PTSD. But that there are many treatment options that can help the whole family cope and improve their relationships and their mental health.

The National Center for PTSD (2007a) offers a number of helpful suggestions for family members of people with PTSD. They acknowledge that family members frequently feel helpless and don't know what to do. Fortunately, there are a few specific steps that will help. They recommend that family members make sure to also take care of themselves while caring for their family member and to remember that no one expects that they will have all the answers. Social support is one of the most important factors and indeed is likely the key to understanding the link between PTSD and intimate relationship problems (Monson et al., 2009). Here are some ways to help (National Center for PTSD, 2007a):

1. Learn about PTSD. Family members should learn as much as they can about PTSD. That will help them understand what their family member is going through and help them better handle the effects of PTSD.
2. Support the family member in the health care system by offering to go to doctor appointments or making sure that they comply with needed treatments.

3. Be willing to listen and also to understand when their family member doesn't feel like talking.

4. Do family activities together, like having dinner, or possibly going to a movie (although going to a movie may be too triggering in the early days).

5. Take a walk together or engage in some other form of family exercise. This helps downregulate stress and elevate mood.

6. Encourage family members to reach out to other family members and close friends. PTSD will be easier to cope with if partners are connected to others who can help share the load. Caregivers need to make sure that their needs are also being met so that they are better able to "be there" for their family member with PTSD.

SUMMARY

As we have described, PTSD can have a significant negative effect on families. In spite of difficulties, it is possible for family members to band together and weather the storm of PTSD. Dolores Davis described how difficult it was to cope with her husband's PTSD after he returned from Vietnam. His symptoms worsened significantly after he lost his job, and he became more paranoid. He was prone to sudden fits of rage, and she had to hold him in the car a few times to keep him from kicking someone else's car. She found it difficult to get support; women in the support groups were really angry and wanted to divorce. She wanted to stay married but was finding it increasing difficult to carry everything alone. She finally collapsed under the strain of running her family business and caring for their four children. She says, "You really have to love your husband and want the marriage to work." She reported that there was light at the end of the tunnel, but it's not quick: "Only by God's grace did we get through it. But we did get through it. I love him more now than I ever did" (Albrecht, 2013).

REFERENCES

Albrecht, B. (2013). *Families share the pain of veterans' PTSD.* Retrieved from http://www.cleveland.com/metro/index.ssf/2013/03/families_share_the_pain_of_vet.html

Byrne, C. A., & Riggs, D. S. (1996). The cycle of trauma: Relationship aggression in male Vietnam veterans with symptoms of posttraumatic stress disorder. *Violence & Victims, 11,* 213–225.

Carlson, E. B., & Ruzek, J. I. (2007). *PTSD and the family.* Retrieved from http://www.ptsd.va.gov/professional/pages/ptsd-and-the-family.asp

Department of Veterans Affairs, Department of Defense. (2010). *VA/DoD clinical practice guideline for the management of posttraumatic stress: Guideline summary.* Retrieved from http://www.healthquality.va.gov/ptsd/Mgmt_of_PTSD_final_92111.pdf

Egeland, B., Jacobvitz, D., & Sroufe, L. A. (1988). Breaking the cycle of abuse. *Child Development, 59,* 1080–1088.

Enlow, M. B., Egeland, B., Carlson, E. A., Blood, E., & Wright, R. J. (2013). Mother-infant attachment and the intergenerational transmission of posttraumatic stress disorder. *Development & Psychopathology,* September 23 [epub ahead of print], 1–26.

Enlow, M. B., Kitts, R. L., Blood, E., Bizarro, A., Hofmeister, M., & Wright, R. J. (2011). Maternal posttraumatic stress symptoms and infant emotional reactivity and emotion regulation. *Infant Behavior & Development, 34*(4), 487–503.

Erbes, C. R., Meis, L. A., Polusny, M. A., & Arbisi, P. A. (2012). Psychiatric distress among spouses of National Guard soldiers prior to combat deployment. *Mental Health in Family Medicine, 9,* 161–169.

Groer, M. W., Davis, M. W., & Hemphill, J. (2002). Postpartum stress: Current concepts and the possible protective role of breast-feeding. *Journal of Obstetric, Gynecologic, & Neonatal Nursing, 31*(4), 411–417.

Hairston, I. S., Waxler, E., Seng, J. S., Fezzey, A. G., Rosenblum, K. L., & Muzik, M. (2011). The role of infant sleep in intergenerational transmission of trauma. *Sleep, 34*(10), 1373–1383.

Hellmuth, J. C., Jaquier, V., Young-Wolff, K., & Sullivan, T. P. (2013). Posttraumatic stress disorder symptom clusters, alcohol misuse and women's use of intimate partner violence. *Journal of Traumatic Stress, 26,* 451–458.

Iliceto, P., Candilera, G., Funaro, D., Pompili, M., Kaplan, K. J., & Markus-Kaplan, M. (2011). Hopelessness, temperament, anger and interpersonal relationships in Holocaust (Shoah) survivors. *Journal of Religion and Health, 50*, 321–329.

Karenian, H., Livaditis, M., Karenian, S., Zafiriadis, K., & Bochtsou, V. (2011). Collective trauma transmission and traumatic reactions among descendants of Armenian refugees. *International Journal of Social Psychiatry, 57*(4), 327–337.

Kendall-Tackett, K. A. (2007). A new paradigm for depression in new mothers: The central role of inflammation and how breastfeeding and anti-inflammatory treatments protect maternal mental health. *International Breastfeeding Journal, 2*, 6. Retrieved from www.internationalbreastfeedingjournal.com/content/2/1/6

Kendall-Tackett, K. A., Cong, Z., & Hale, T. W. (2013). Depression, sleep quality, and maternal well-being in postpartum women with a history of sexual assault: A comparison of breastfeeding, mixed-feeding, and formula-feeding mothers. *Breastfeeding Medicine, 8*(1), 16–22.

Klaric, M., Franciskovic, T., Stevanovic, A., Petrov, B., Jonovska, S., & Moro, I. M. (2011). Marital quality and relationship satisfaction in war veterans and their wives in Bosnia and Herzegovina. *European Journal of Psychotraumatology, 2*, 8077. doi:10.3402/ejpt.v2i0.8077

Kulka, R. A., Schlenger, W. E., Fairbank, J. A., Hough, R. L., Jordan, B. K., & Marmar, C. R. (1990). *Trauma and the Vietnam War generation: Report of findings from the National Vietnam Readjustment Study*. New York, NY: Brunner/Mazel.

Link, P. E., & Palinkas, L. A. (2013). Long-term trajectories and service needs for military families. *Clinical Child & Family Psychological Review, 16*, 376–393.

May, J. (2013). *Veterans, families face effects of PTSD after combat*. Retrieved from http://www.mrt.com/life/article_1ba8f15f-8ce7-551f-b23a-0085a0940eaa.html

Miller, M. W., Reardon, A. F., Wolf, E. J., Prince, L. B., & Hein, C. L. (2013). Alcohol and drug abuse among U.S. veterans: Comparing associations with intimate partner substance abuse and veteran psychopathology. *Journal of Traumatic Stress, 26*, 71–76.

Monson, C. M., Taft, C. T., & Fredman, S. J. (2009). Military-related PTSD and intimate relationships: From description to theory-driven research and intervention development. *Clinical Psychological Review, 29*(8), 707–714.

Muzik, M., Bocknek, E. L., Broderick, A., Richardson, P., Rosenblum, K. L., Thelen, K., & Seng, J. S. (2013). Mother-infant bonding impairment across the first 6 months postpartum: The primacy of psychopathology in women with childhood abuse and neglect histories. *Archives of Women's Mental Health, 16,* 29–38.

National Center for PTSD. (2007a). *Helping a family member who has PTSD.* Retrieved from http://www.ptsd.va.gov/public/pages/helping-family-member.asp

National Center for PTSD. (2007b). *Partners of veterans with PTSD: Common problems.* Retrieved from http://www.ptsd.va.gov/public/pages/partners-of-vets.asp

National Center for PTSD. (2010). *Effects of PTSD on family.* Retrieved from http://www.ptsd.va.gov/public/pages/effects-ptsd-family.asp

National Center for PTSD. (n.d.). *Understanding PTSD.* Retrieved from http://www.ptsd.va.gov/public/understanding_ptsd/booklet.pdf

Palosaari, E., Punamaki, R. L., Qouta, S., & Diab, M. (2013). Intergenerational effects of war trauma among Palestinian families mediated via psychological maltreatment. *Child Abuse & Neglect.* doi:10.1016/j.chiabu.2013.04.006

Portney, C. (2003). *Intergenerational transmission of trauma: An introduction for the clinician.* Retrieved from http://www.psychiatrictimes.com/articles/intergenerational-transmission-trauma-introduction-clinician

President's Commission on Mental Health. (1978). *Mental health problems of Vietnam-era veterans* (Vol. 3). Washington, DC: U.S. Government Printing Office.

Price, J. L., & Stevens, S. P. (2009). *Partners of veterans with PTSD: Research findings.* Retrieved from http://www.ptsd.va.gov/professional/pages/partners_of_vets_research_findings.asp

Renshaw, K. D., & Caska, C. M. (2012). Relationship distress in partners of combat veterans: The role of partners' perceptions of posttraumatic stress symptoms. *Behavior Therapy, 43,* 416–426.

Roan, S. (2013). *How PTSD hurts families: "My dad never really came back from the war": The daughter of a veteran speaks for the often-forgotten victims of posttraumatic stress syndrome in the military: Kids.* Retrieved from http://www.takepart.com/article/2013/03/19/suffer-little-children

Seng, J. S., Sperlich, M. A., Low, L. K., Ronis, D. L., Muzik, M., & Liberzon, I. (2013). Childhood abuse history, posttraumatic stress disorder, postpartum mental health, and bonding: A prospective cohort study. *Journal of Midwifery and Women's Health, 58*(1), 57–68.

Shea, M. T., Reddy, M. K., Tyrka, A. R., & Sevin, E. (2013). Risk factors for post-deployment posttraumatic stress disorder in national guard/ reserve service members. *Psychiatry Research, 210*(3), 1042–1048.

Strathearn, L., Mamun, A. A., Najman, J. M., & O'Callaghan, M. J. (2009). Does breastfeeding protect against substantiated child abuse and neglect? A 15-year cohort study. *Pediatrics, 123*(2), 483–493. doi:123/2/483 [pii] 10.1542/peds.2007-3546

Zamorski, M. A., & Wiens-Kinkaid, M. E. (2013). Cross-sectional prevalence survey of intimate partner violence perpetration and victimization in Canadian military personnel. *BMC Public Health, 13*, 1019. doi:10.1186/1471-2458-13-1019

APPENDIX

Resources for Families of Persons With PTSD

Compiled from Healing Hearts of Hope (healingheartsinhope. com/crisis.html).

- The National Suicide Prevention Lifeline is a 24-hour hotline for anyone in emotional distress: 1-800-273-TALK (8255). There is also an online lifeline chat available from 5 p.m. to 1 a.m. EST, weekdays.
- The Veterans Crisis Line connects veterans in crisis and their families and friends with VA responders through a 24/7 hotline: 1-800-273-TALK (8255). There is also a 24/7 online confidential veterans chat.
- The National Domestic Violence Hotline offers 24/7 anonymous access to shelters and domestic violence programs as well as legal advocacy, public education, and training: 1-800-799-SAFE (7233).
- The National Sexual Assault Hotline operated by RAINN (Rape, Abuse, and Incest National Network) is a 24/7 resource to link victims with counseling and legal advice: 1-800-656-HOPE (4673). There is also a national sexual assault online hotline for text messaging.
- The National Child Abuse Hotline is a 24/7 resource you can contact if you suspect that a child is being abused, if you fear that you might hurt your child, or if you have been abused: 1-800-4-A-CHILD (422-4453).

General Resources for Family and Loved Ones

Good resources are available to help family members care for themselves while caring for their loved one with PTSD.

- Most U.S. states have a 211 referral line that connects people with important community services (employment, food pantries, housing, support groups, etc.). Dial 2-1-1.

- The SIDRAN Institute is a nonprofit organization that helps people understand, recover from, and treat traumatic stress and offers a referral list of therapists for PTSD. You can contact the help desk via www.sidran.org/help-desk/get-help or by leaving a confidential voicemail: 1-410-825-8888.
- The National Alliance on Mental Illness (NAMI) offers a Family-to-Family Education Program for caregivers of people with severe mental illness. You can also contact NAMI at info@nami.org or call the Information Help Line: 1-800-950-NAMI (6264).

Resources for Loved Ones of Veterans and Service Members

Some of the resources listed above help veterans and service members, as do these additional resources:

- The VA Caregiver Support program provides services to support family members who are taking care of a veteran: 1-855-260-3274.
- VA's Coaching Into Care program helps family and friends of returning veterans find the right words to help their loved one get into care. For free, confidential coaching, contact coachingintocare@va.gov or call 1-888-823-7458.
- The Vet Center Combat Call Center is a 24/7 call center for combat veterans and their families to talk about their military experience or difficulties readjusting to civilian life: 1-877-WAR-VETS.
- The Defense Centers of Excellence (DCoE) 24/7 Outreach Center offers information and consultation in mental health and traumatic brain injury: 1-866-966-1020. DCoE also offers e-mail (resources@dcoeoutreach.org) and online chat support.
- The National Resource Directory links to over 10,000 services and resources that support recovery, rehabilitation, and reintegration for wounded, ill, and injured service members and veterans, as well as their families and those who support them.

- Give an Hour is a nonprofit organization offering free mental health services to U.S. military personnel and their families affected by Iraq and Afghanistan.
- You can find more resources on the Web Links: Section page for Families, Military Resources, and Veterans Service Organizations.

Resources for Children With a Parent Who Has PTSD

Children respond to their parents' PTSD symptoms. A child may behave like the parent to try to connect with him or her. Some children take on an adult role to fill in for the parent with PTSD. If children do not get help with their feelings, it can lead to problems at school, in relationships, or with emotions (like worry, fear, or sadness).

- MilitaryKidsConnect (MKC) is an online community for military children (ages 6–17) with resources for children to give support before, during, and after a parent's or caregiver's deployment.
- Sesame Street offers a Talk, Listen, Connect parent toolkit to help military families coping with deployment.
- It is important for children to know that a parent's PTSD symptoms are not the children's fault. An interactive workbook for teens may help: "Finding My Way: A Teen's Guide to Living With a Parent Who Has Experienced Trauma."
- You can find more resources on the Web Links: Children and Teens page.

Burnout, Compassion Fatigue, and Clinician Self-Care

There is a cost to caring. Professionals who listen to clients' stories of fear, pain, and suffering may feel similar fear, pain, and suffering because they care. . . . Those who have enormous capacity for feeling and expression [of] empathy tend to be more at risk of compassion stress.
—Charles Figley, 1995, p. 1

elf-care is critical when someone works with clients or patients who have experienced trauma. The work itself is hard. The needs of these patients can become overwhelming, and burnout rates in caretakers are high. Providers might also be dealing with their own trauma history. Hearing about the traumatic experiences of others can trigger their own trauma memories. Burnout is possible, as are compassion fatigue and secondary traumatic stress. Burnout is a gradual process. Secondary traumatic stress can be gradual but can also happen suddenly. We'll describe each of these in the following, along with the causes and consequences and what providers can do about them.

BURNOUT

Herbert Freudenberger first defined burnout "as a condition of fatigue or frustration produced by dedication to a cause expected to give positive results that conflicts with a reality that does not correspond to the professional's expectations" (cited in Bortoletti et al., 2012, p. 159). Burnout is a process during which a person disconnects from work and relationships. The professional's own needs are neglected in favor of the work.

In the past 30 years, burnout has been noted in a wide variety of people-intensive professions: mental health, emergency services, nursing, police work, social work, and medicine. Burnout is caused by unrelenting stress and happens when someone feels overwhelmed and unable to meet the constant demands of his or her job or situation (Smith, Segal, & Segal, 2013). When everything looks bleak and that outlook persists for weeks or months, burnout may be the culprit. Burnout signals the end of active coping and marks the beginning of passive coping and withdrawal, with associated resource depletion (Bianchi, Boffy, Hingray, Truchot, & Laurent, 2013).

What Causes Burnout?

A variety of factors can put someone at risk for burnout. The self-help organization HelpGuide.org (Smith, Segal, & Segal, 2013) notes that "burnout often arises from excessive demands that are internally imposed (such as having very high expectations of yourself), or externally imposed (by family, job or society). It occurs when you are unable to meet these demands, become frustrated, and deplete your energy through unrelenting stress" (p. 1). Following is a summary of some of the common causes.

Overwork. Work that is "never done" puts people at risk for burnout. Many providers working with traumatized people often work a high number of hours. The needs are so many that there doesn't seem to be any way to meet them all. When someone struggles to meet his or her daily demands with a tired body, mental and emotional fatigue are not far behind. In addition, working a high number of hours can affect relationships with family and friends and could result in providers' having limited social support. Long working hours also decrease the amount of time available for relaxation, exercise, sleep, and other forms of self-care.

The number of hours is only one of the factors related to work. There are factors related to the job itself. According to HelpGuide.org, jobs most likely to lead to burnout were those in which employees felt little or no control over their work, felt unrecognized or unrewarded for their work, felt that the job expectations were unclear or overly demanding, felt that the work was monotonous or boring, and felt high pressure (Smith et al., 2013). A study of 239 primary care doctors from the Republic of Srpska found that age and length of service also contributed to burnout: The longer the length of service, the higher number of burnout symptoms they showed (Stanetic & Tesanovic, 2013).

Unrealistic Expectations. Providers may also place unrealistic expectations on themselves. People who burnout may feel that they are expected to be many things to many people and that they need to take on too many responsibilities without enough help from others. They may believe that they can do it alone, not realizing how much they need a good support network.

Lack of Sense of Coherence. Another personality trait related to burnout is lack of sense of coherence. Sense of coherence is a personality trait that is related to coping with stressful situations. People with a high sense of coherence perceive life as comprehensible, manageable, and meaningful, and this protects them from burnout. A study of student nurses found that a low sense of coherence was related to high burnout symptoms (Skodova & Lajciakova, 2013). In contrast, self-esteem was not related to burnout. They also found that their intervention to improve the students' coping strategies decreased their symptoms of burnout.

Perfectionism. Perfectionism can also be a setup for burnout. Burnout can happen when providers believe that they have to do all things well or that their best is never good enough. Since no one can be perfect, a perfectionist may simply give up, disengaging from relationships and adopting a cynical *what-difference-does-it-make* attitude. Perfectionists often have a pessimistic view of the world. They often feel the need to be in control and are reluctant to delegate. Finally, they tend to be high-achieving, "type A" personalities (Smith et al., 2013).

In moderation, many of these traits are admirable. Perfectionists want to do a good job in everything that they do. And they may be motivated by their compassion for others. But like any good thing, perfectionism can be taken too far. And when it is, it puts the perfectionist at risk for burnout.

Codependency and Overinvolvement. Codependency is a word that has been so overused it is almost a cliché. There is nothing wrong with being concerned about and caring for other people. In fact, that's a good thing. But a provider's desire to help others needs to balance with self-care. Providers' beliefs about helping also affect their susceptibility to burnout. Of particular interest is the construct of unmitigated communion (UC). People with this interpersonal style tend not to have reciprocal relationships and are too involved in the needs of others. In many caretaking situations, it is appropriate for the clinician to be the one giving. However, it is of concern when all the clinician's relationships are this way. The person who takes care of everyone's needs with no reciprocal relationships is at high risk for burning out.

Helgeson and Fritz (1998) describe some beliefs associated with UC that might be problematic for clinicians, especially those working with trauma survivors.

- **Attachments.** The clinician has a hard time connecting with others, fears abandonment, and does not feel sure that people love him or her.
- **Relationships.** The clinician has a negative view of himself or herself or others, feels that others perceive him or her negatively, or does not enjoy helping people but rather feels coerced into it.
- **Social support.** The clinician lacks genuine support, is always the one to give support and never receives it, or likes the sense of control he or she has by being the "support provider."
- **Motivations for helping.** The clinician is motivated to help others so that people will think well of him or her, rather than because he or she has a genuine concern for the well-being of others.

Common Signs of Burnout

A number of signs may indicate that someone is experiencing burnout. Providers might find that they are experiencing any one of these, or several.

Negative Emotions. Everyone occasionally feels angry or sad. However, when anger or sadness becomes something experienced every day, that may be a sign of burnout. Another aspect of negative feelings is when people begin to doubt what they're supposed to do. They may feel like imposters. Other negative emotions include feeling hopeless, drained, detached from others, bored, and resentful. Providers may feel stuck in a situation they cannot change and derive little satisfaction from their work. Some of these negative feelings could be related to unrealistic expectations providers may place on themselves about what they're supposed to be like. They may believe that caregivers should give endlessly. They may also feel that they can't say no to anyone or set boundaries on when and where they will provide care.

A study of 48 OB/GYNs from Brazil found that emotional exhaustion and dehumanization were the most common types of burnout symptoms in the sample (Bortoletti et al., 2012). Emotional exhaustion was characterized by feeling no energy after a day of work, waking up feeling tired, having no stamina for anything else, needing to put forth great effort to get up and go to work, and feeling that work consumes all available energy. In the dehumanization factor, the participants scored higher in burnout if they said they had become "tougher" in the course of their time on the job or became insensitive to the problems of people at work. In addition, dehumanization was higher if they reported being more "technical" and less "human" in their work. A high rate of negative organizational conditions contributed to the triggering of these burnout symptoms.

A study of 226 Greek–Cypriot psychiatric nurses found low rates of burnout (Karanikola & Papthanassoglou, 2013). But 10% of the sample reported clinically significant depression and anxiety symptoms. The authors used the Maslach Burnout Inventory (MBI) to measure burnout. The MBI is a highly validated measure of burnout that assesses burnout in education, human service, and business professionals. There are three scales in the MBI: emotional exhaustion, depersonalization, and personal accomplishment. In the study, two scales of the MBI were significantly associated with depression and anxiety: emotional exhaustion and depersonalization. The authors concluded that their findings suggest that depression, anxiety, and burnout may have a common neurobiological etiology, possibly due to a dysregulated inflammatory/neuroendocrine response.

Another study tested whether burnout was an entity that was distinct from major depression (Bianchi et al., 2013). In this study, the researchers compared 46 people with burnout,

46 patients with major depressive disorder, and 453 people who had neither burnout nor depression. They found that most people in the burnout group also met the criteria for depression. The authors stated that their data did not support burnout and depression as separate entities but that the two were in fact the same underlying condition: depression.

Interpersonal Problems. Problems with other people can also be a symptom of burnout. Providers may feel like withdrawing from others or may feel frustrated with people or find themselves overreacting to perceived misdeeds. They may become abrasive or harsh. People in the helping professions who are burning out may find themselves feeling cynical and insensitive to the needs of people in their care—and this is when the situation can become dangerous.

Health Problems. Burnout can also be associated with a wide range of health problems. These problems include aches and pains, colds, headaches, and chronic fatigue. People with burnout often have major depressive disorder (Bianchi et al., 2013). There is evidence that burnout increases the risk of disease due to dysregulation of the hypothalamic–pituitary–adrenal (HPA) axis and an upregulation of the inflammatory response system. Sleep is disturbed. All this contributes to increased risk of heart disease, hypertension, diabetes, and metabolic syndrome (Skodova & Lajciakova, 2013). Disturbed sleep is enough to cause serious health problems. In a study of law enforcement officers, poor sleep quality was associated with stress, depression, and burnout. In addition, sleep duration was more strongly associated with metabolic syndrome than sleep quality or mental health (Yoo & Franke, 2013).

Loss of Enthusiasm and Feelings of Meaninglessness. Burnout is often a time of existential crisis. Providers may find themselves questioning, perhaps for the first time, their role and the work they do. Everything seems like too much trouble—things seem to make no difference. Nothing seems to matter. They may find themselves saying, "Why bother?" or "Who cares?" They may even feel as if they don't know themselves anymore.

Substance Abuse and Unhealthy Behaviors. To cope with their feelings, providers may turn to alcohol or drugs. They may also find themselves eating too much, smoking too much, and drinking too much coffee. All of these activities are physically depleting and compound the problem.

What Providers Can Do About Burnout

You may have noticed that many of the symptoms of burnout are similar to those of depression. Not surprisingly, one aspect of burnout can be chronic depression. Depending on how bad the symptoms are, providers may need to seek the assistance of a (or another) mental health professional. Fortunately, there are a number of positive steps providers can take.

Stop Denying. When someone is burned out, he or she often doesn't recognize it. The first step on recovering from burnout is to recognize it and resolve to take some positive action.

Get Reconnected. People have a natural tendency to withdraw from others when they are under stress. Burnout compounds this by making people irritable and impatient. Clinicians in the throes of burnout may also withdraw from others for fear that others will discover that they are not perfect.

For someone who is burned out, it's vital to start reconnecting with others. Ideally, he or she should start with family by setting aside time to be with his or her partner and children. Reconnecting with friends is also important. The goal is to form reciprocal relationships, those in which both parties give to and support each other.

Set Some Boundaries. Clinicians suffering from burnout may find that they have been taking on too much in several areas of their lives. They may be the ones everyone comes to with their problems. Or they may try to do everything themselves and have a hard time saying no.

So an important recovery skill is learning to set reasonable limits, and stop trying to meet everyone's needs. This doesn't mean that providers need to stop caring about others. In fact, self-care increases our ability to care for others (Figley, 2010). When a request to do something comes in, realistically evaluate whether it is possible at that time. When someone freely chooses to do something, it will be much more enjoyable than if doing so feels coerced.

Get Some Help With the Work. Another recovery strategy is to try to do less work by delegating or involving others. We know that this is easier said than done. Clinicians should recognize that it doesn't always need to be them. That being said, sometimes it really does need to be them. In those cases, it's important to delegate other work that can be done by someone else.

Some Final Thoughts

Burnout may feel like a hopeless situation. Fortunately, it is not. For more information, refer to some of the resources at the end of this book. There is a light at the end of this tunnel.

COMPASSION STRESS AND FATIGUE

People who hear about traumatic events that others have experienced can be traumatized and even develop posttraumatic stress disorder (Figley, 1995). This is true for providers as well as for family members and friends. This phenomenon has gone by several names: *covictimization, vicarious traumatization, countertransference*, and *emotional contagion*. Figley (1995) suggests instead the terms *compassion stress* and *compassion fatigue*.

Unlike burnout, compassion fatigue can happen suddenly. When patients recount the circumstances leading to their trauma, it is not unusual for clinicians who hear this information to experience intense emotions. Providers may feel guilt that they have not been through the horrific events patients describe (Friedman, 2001). They may also feel a sense of powerlessness that they were unable to protect a patient, even when they rationally know that they could never have done so (e.g., the event took place long before they knew the patient).

Although it is natural for providers to feel bad about what their patients have gone through, it gets to be a problem when they begin to have symptoms of PTSD. For example, they might start experiencing intrusive thoughts, nightmares about their patient's experiences, or emotional numbing. All these experiences can cloud professional judgment to such an extent that they try to "rescue" their patients or avoid the patients' references to their traumas, which can lead to severe personal distress (DeAngelis, 2002; Friedman, 2001).

Compassion fatigue appears to be relatively common among those who work with abuse survivors. In a national study of 1,000 women psychotherapists, those with the highest levels of exposure to details about patients' previous sexual abuse experiences had the highest levels of trauma symptoms. However, spirituality offered some protection. Clinicians who reported that they had a spiritual life seemed to do well even when exposed to the abuse histories of their patients. The clinicians who saw the highest numbers of abuse survivors also reported the highest levels of spiritual well-being (Brady, Guy, Poelstra, & Brokaw, 1999).

Secondary traumatic stress can also happen in medical settings. In a random sample of 464 labor and delivery nurses, 35% reported moderate to severe secondary trauma from being exposed to traumatic births (Beck & Gable, 2012). Ten percent reported high secondary traumatic stress, and 14% reported severe secondary stress. In Beck and Gable's study, secondary trauma was more likely when actions of the doctors or other people in authority caused harm to the mother and baby, and when the nurses felt helpless and powerless to intervene. One nurse described her experience as follows.

> The physician violated her. A perfect delivery turned violent. I felt like an accomplice to a crime. The doctor treated her like a piece of dirt. After the birth of the baby, he proceeded to put his hand inside her practically halfway up his arm to start pulling the placenta out . . . I felt like I was watching a rape. (Beck & Gable, 2012)

Another nurse described the sounds that still haunt her:

> Whenever I hear a patient screaming, I will flash back to a patient who had an unmedicated (not even local) caesarean section and to the wailing of a mother when we were coding her baby in the delivery room. I feel like I will never get these sounds/images out of my head even though they occurred more than 10 years ago. (Beck & Gable, 2012)

A study of 782 rescue workers in Italy also found that vicarious traumatization symptoms were common (Argentero & Setti, 2011). In this study, the intrusion symptoms were most common, with 52% reporting that their hearts pound faster when thinking about the victims they worked with. The least common symptom was nightmares. The authors also considered the construct of engagement, the extent to which emergency workers felt energized by the work that they did and experienced increased self-efficacy as a result. The authors found that rescue workers in a supportive work environment had significantly lower symptoms of vicarious traumatization and posttraumatic stress symptoms. Role clarity (knowing what was expected from them at work) was also related to lower posttraumatic stress symptoms.

For 224 mental health workers working with the military, the rate of secondary traumatic stress was 19.2% (Cieslak et al., 2013). The factors related to higher levels of secondary traumatic stress were personal history of trauma, complaints of having too many patients, and more negative appraisals of impact caused by indirect exposure to trauma. More work-related paperwork was also associated with secondary traumatic stress.

According to Figley (1995), secondary traumatic stress is a natural consequence of caring that happens between two people:

one who has been traumatized and the other who is affected by the first person's trauma. It's not necessarily a problem, but rather a natural by-product of caring for those who have experienced trauma. However, countertransference happens only within the context of psychotherapy, and it is a negative consequence of therapy that should be prevented or eliminated. It is described in the following section.

Countertransference

Countertransference is a psychoanalytic term that has relevance to trauma work. In general terms, it refers to something in the client's story triggering a response in the clinician. With regard to trauma research, it happens when a client's story triggers memories of abuse or trauma in the clinician. Vicarious traumatization can occur in the absence of previous trauma experienced by the provider. In contrast, countertransference occurs when the patient's stories of trauma are similar to traumatic events that the provider has experienced. Countertransference is more likely to occur when patients reveal histories similar to the clinician's own story (Friedman, 2001).

Trauma histories are fairly common in both mental health and medical providers and are often found in those who work with either victims or perpetrators of abuse. For example, in a survey of 645 professionals who conduct sexual abuse evaluations, 17% reported a history of sexual abuse, and 7% reported a history of physical abuse (Nuttal & Jackson, 1994). In the Nurses' Health Study II (N = 54,200), 13% of nurses reported intimate partner emotional abuse, 4% psychological abuse, and 25% at least one incident of physical or sexual abuse, with or without co-occurring psychological abuse (Jun, Rich-Edwards, Boynton-Jarrett, & Wright, 2008).

In another study of 501 clinicians, Little and Hamby (1996) found that 32% reported a history of child sexual abuse. Therapists who had been sexually abused reported more difficulties with countertransference and boundary issues. However, gender differences were a stronger source of variance than past abuse. Female clinicians were more likely to report that sexual abuse was more difficult to treat, that they screened regularly for sexual abuse in their patients, and that they used more coping strategies in their work than male clinicians.

In a sample of 150 clinicians working with sex offenders, 37% of females and 27% of males had a history of child sexual abuse (Hilton, Jennings, Drugge, & Stephens, 1995). Interestingly, those clinicians with a history of sexual abuse reported either that it had no effect on their work or that its effects were positive. The authors offered one possible explanation for their finding: The overall abuse experiences of most of their subjects were relatively mild.

Finally, a study of 323 nurses revealed that 13% had a history of child sexual abuse. In comparing the work of abused and nonabused nurses, there were no significant differences between the two groups on whether they thought patients should be screened for past abuse (most thought nurses should screen) and whether they thought patients would be upset if they asked the patients about past abuse (slightly over half thought that these questions would upset patients). Past history did seem to influence the nurses' level of comfort in talking about abuse with patients. Twenty-three percent of the abused nurses and 34% of the nonabused nurses felt "extremely comfortable" listening to patients' stories of abuse. On the other end, 9.5% of abused nurses and 3.6% of nonabused nurses reported that they would be "extremely uncomfortable" talking to patients about abuse. For the nurses who were moderately comfortable, there were no differences between the abused and nonabused groups. The nurses who thought that all patients should be screened offered the following caveats: The nurse needs to be skilled in knowing how to ask and must have the resources in place to respond to any needs that arise (Gallop, McKeever, Toner, Lance, & Lueck, 1995).

Symptoms of Compassion Fatigue

In addition to symptoms of PTSD, additional symptoms of compassion fatigue are similar to those of burnout. Describing compassion fatigue in physicians, Pfifferling and Gilley (2000) describe the following symptoms:

- Abusing drugs, alcohol, or food
- Anger and irritability
- Blaming
- Chronic lateness
- Hopelessness and depression
- Diminished sense of personal accomplishment
- Chronic exhaustion (physical or emotional)
- Sleep disturbances
- Working too many hours
- Frequent headaches or gastrointestinal complaints
- High self-expectations and low self-esteem
- Hypertension
- Inability to maintain balance of empathy and objectivity
- Diminished ability to feel joy

A study of 7,584 physicians in Argentina examined the relationships between compassion satisfaction and compassion fatigue (Gleichgerrcht & Decety, 2013). It found that women displayed higher values on empathic concern but also felt more devalued by patients and their caregivers and by their colleagues. Empathic concern, which was related to compassion satisfaction, was related to altruism and perspective taking in both men and women. Clinicians experienced benefits from helping if they were able to take another's perspective and were motivated to help by someone else's need. These benefits acted as a buffer to job stress.

Participants who had high levels of compassion fatigue, with little or no compassion satisfaction, scored highest on personal distress and alexithymia. Alexithymia included difficulties describing or identifying emotions, a tendency to ignore one's own emotions and personal distress, and self-oriented negative emotions when witnessing someone in distress. It was related to both burnout and compassion fatigue (Gleichgerrcht & Decety, 2013). Empathy toward others, and the ability to infer the thoughts and feelings of others while understanding that they differ from one's own, resulted in higher levels of compassion satisfaction. In other words, physicians were likely to have warm feelings when helping someone in distress if they had empathy accuracy and empathic concern and could take another's perspective. If they had low levels of perspective taking and high levels of personal distress, then burnout and secondary traumatic stress emerged.

PROFESSIONAL SELF-CARE

*First, **do no harm to yourself** in the line of duty when helping/treating others. Second, attend to your physical, social, emotional, and spiritual needs as a way of ensuring high-quality services to those who look to you for support as a human being.*
— Charles Figley, 2010

In light of the inherent challenges in working with trauma survivors, self-care for clinicians is essential. Gleichgerrcht and Decety (2013) describe how clinical empathy is essential to quality of care, high patient satisfaction, adherence to treatment, and fewer malpractice complaints. Without self-care, providers are impaired and their patients, and the clinician's own family, suffer. Vicarious traumatization and countertransference can impair both professional judgment and personal mental health.

Friedman (2001) describes how clinicians may find themselves trapped in a vicious cycle of increasing symptoms and increasing ineffectiveness with clients, which leads them to plunge themselves into their work further. Some specific suggestions for breaking this cycle are described in the following.

Recognize the Occupational Hazards

The first step to breaking the vicious cycle of compassion fatigue is recognizing that there are unique hazards associated with working with trauma survivors. This may also involve recognizing one's own vulnerability and acknowledging, perhaps for the first time, one's own history of childhood abuse or other trauma. Clinicians' own trauma history can eventually make them more effective in their work. But it also brings with it an increased vulnerability.

Suggestions for Self-Care

Once providers recognize their vulnerability, they can take specific steps to counter it. Figley (2010) teaches that self-care is essential for all those who work with traumatized people. Lack of self-care is not noble: It leads to clinicians who are impaired. In an article for physicians, Pfifferling and Gilley (2000) recommend that providers in the throes of compassion fatigue avoid making major decisions. These types of decisions include quitting their job, making major purchases, getting a divorce, or having an affair. The behaviors will not improve compassion fatigue symptoms but will likely lead to even more problems. They also recommend that providers not blame others, complain with others, or initiate legal action against their workplace. Following are some additional suggestions for self-care for providers who work with traumatized people (Friedman, 2001):

Don't Go It Alone. Providers should acknowledge that some patients require the care of more than one clinician. Clinical work is often a solitary activity, even when providers share office space with others. A recent qualitative study of seven Canadian mental health professionals also emphasized the need for social support (Marriage & Marriage, 2005). This included debriefing with peers, having a supervision group with psychologist and psychiatrist colleagues, and having supportive family (especially the spouse) and friends. If providers find that a patient's story is stirring up memories in them, they should consider seeking counseling themselves.

Limit Involvement. An important type of self-care for providers is learning not to carry patients' concerns once they leave the office. Providers should strive to keep firm boundaries between work and home life. Some therapists described a need to compartmentalize and to keep work at work (Marriage & Marriage, 2005). For example, providers may resolve to leave their briefcases in the office or not to think about clients once they are on their way home. This way they can continue to be connected and caring in the office while minimizing the emotional toll of this type of caring. Another strategy for providers is to limit the number of trauma cases they see by balancing out their caseloads with less severely affected patients.

Develop a Specific Self-Care Plan. This strategy applies to anyone doing stressful work, but it is especially important for those who care for trauma survivors: Providers should take time to take care of their bodies. This means getting enough sleep, eating nutritious foods, exercising, connecting with others, and maintaining a spiritual life. This might also mean taking time alone every day. Practicing mindfulness, which can ground them and keep them from being pulled away in a thousand different directions, can be particularly helpful (Pfifferling & Gilley, 2000). Some other examples of self-care could include taking a walk in the middle of the day, getting a massage, or making a date with a friend. Providers should have hobbies and things they enjoy that are not related to their work. In short, providers should model for their patients how to live a balanced life.

SUMMARY

There are many unique aspects to working with traumatized patients that make it easy to get overwhelmed. It is important that providers avoid isolation, connect with others, and make time for activities away from work. If providers are going to be available to their patients, they must take time to refresh, refuel, and restore balance. In this way, they can continue to be healthy helpers.

REFERENCES

Argentero, P., & Setti, I. (2011). Engagement and vicarious traumatization in rescue workers. *International Archives of Occupational and Environmental Health, 84*, 67–75.

Beck, C. T., & Gable, R. K. (2012). A mixed methods study of secondary traumatic stress in labor and delivery nurses. *Journal of Obstetric, Gynecologic, and Neonatal Nursing, 41*(6), 747–760. doi:10.1111/j.1552-6909 2012.01.386x

Bianchi, R., Boffy, C., Hingray, C., Truchot, D., & Laurent, E. (2013). Comparative symptomatology of burnout and depression. *Journal of Health Psychology, 18*(6), 782–787.

Bortoletti, F. F., Benevides-Pereira, A. M. T., Vasconcellos, E. G., Siqueira, J. O., Araujo, E., Nardozza, L. M. M., . . . Moron, A. F. (2012). Triggering risk factors of the burnout syndrome in OB/GYN physicians from a Reference Public University of Brazil. *ISRN Obstetrics and Gynecology, 2012*. doi:10.5402/2012/593876

Brady, J. L., Guy, J. D., Poelstra, P. L., & Brokaw, B. F. (1999). Vicarious traumatization, spirituality, and the treatment of sexual abuse survivors: A national survey of women psychotherapists. *Professional Psychology: Research and Practice, 30*, 386–393.

Cieslak, R., Anderson, V., Bock, J., Moore, B. A., Peterson, A. L., & Benight, C. C. (2013). Secondary traumatic stress among mental health providers working with the military. *Journal of Nervous & Mental Disease, 201*, 917–925.

DeAngelis, T. (2002, July/August). Normalizing practitioners' stress. *Monitor on Psychology*, 62–64.

Figley, C. (1995). Compassion fatigue as secondary traumatic stress disorder: An overview. In C. R. Figley (Ed.), *Compassion fatigue: Coping with secondary traumatic stress disorder in those who treat the traumatized* (pp. 1–20). New York, NY: Brunner/Mazel.

Figley, C. (2010). *Standards of self care*. Retrieved from http://www. greencross.org/index.php?option=com_content&view=article&id =184&Itemid=124

Friedman, M. J. (2001). *Posttraumatic stress disorder: The latest assessment and treatment strategies*. Kansas City, MO: Compact Clinicals.

Gallop, R., McKeever, P., Toner, B., Lancee, W., & Lueck, M. (1995). Inquiring about childhood sexual abuse as part of the nursing history: Opinions of abuse and nonabused nurses. *Archives of Psychiatric Nursing, 9*, 146–151.

Gleichgerrcht, E., & Decety, J. (2013). Empathy in clinical practice: How individual dispositions, gender, and experience moderate empathic concern, burnout, and emotional distress in physicians. *PLoS One, 8*(4), e61526. Retrieved from http://www. plosone.org

Helgeson, V. S., & Fritz, H. L. (1998). A theory of unmitigated communion. *Personality & Social Psychology Review, 2*, 173–183.

Hilton, N. Z., Jennings, K. T., Drugge, J., & Stephens, J. (1995). Childhood sexual abuse among clinicians working with sex offenders. *Journal of Interpersonal Violence, 10*, 525–532.

Jun, H. J., Rich-Edwards, J. W., Boynton-Jarrett, R., & Wright, R. J. (2008). Intimate partner violence and cigarette smoking: Association between smoking risk and psychological abuse with and without co-occurrence of physical and sexual abuse. *American Journal of Public Health, 98*, 527–535.

Karanikola, M. N. K., & Papthanassoglou, E. E. D. (2013). Exploration of the burnout syndrome occurrence among mental health nurses in Cyprus. *Archives of Psychiatric Nursing, 27*, 319–326.

Little, L., & Hamby, S. (1996). Impact of a clinician's sexual abuse history, gender, and theoretical orientation on treatment issues related to childhood sexual abuse. *Professional Psychology: Research and Practice, 27*, 617–625.

Marriage, S., & Marriage, K. (2005). Too many sad stories: Clinician stress and coping. *Canadian Child and Adolescent Psychiatric Review, 14*(4), 114–117.

Nuttal, R., & Jackson, H. (1994). Personal history of childhood abuse among clinicians. *Child Abuse & Neglect, 18*, 455–472.

Pfifferling, J.-H., & Gilley, K. (2000). Overcoming compassion fatigue. *Family Practice Management, 7*(4), 39–44.

Skodova, Z., & Lajciakova, P. (2013). The effect of personality traits and psychosocial training on burnout syndrome among healthcare students. *Nurse Education Today, 33*, 1311–1315.

Smith, M., Segal, J., & Segal, R. (2013). *Preventing burnout: Signs, symptoms, causes, and coping strategies.* Retrieved from http://www. helpguide.org/mental/burnout_signs_symptoms.htm

Stanetic, K., & Tesanovic, G. (2013). Influence of age and length of service on the level of stress and burnout syndrome. *Medicinski Pregled, 66*(3–4), 153–162.

Yoo, H., & Franke, W. D. (2013). Sleep habits, mental health, and the metabolic syndrome in law enforcement officers. *Journal of Occupational and Environmental Medicine, 55*(1), 99–103.

Evidence-Based Treatments for Trauma, Posttraumatic Stress Disorder, and Related Conditions

ver the past 30 years, multiple evidence-based psychological and pharmacologic treatments have been developed for the treatment of posttraumatic stress disorder (PTSD) (Foa, Keane, Friedman, & Cohen, 2009). Several national and international treatment guidelines have also been created to assist clinicians and clients with the selection and utilization of the best evidence-based treatments for PTSD. For example, the International Traumatic Stress Studies (ISTSS) developed treatment guidelines for PTSD (Foa et al., 2009). The U.S. Department of Veterans Affairs

(VA) and Department of Defense (DoD) also developed clinical practice guidelines for management of posttraumatic stress (Management of Post-Traumatic Stress Working Group, 2010). These guidelines are based on systematic reviews and meta-analyses that have examined the efficacy of existing treatments in reducing symptoms of PTSD (Foa et al., 2009; Forbes et al., 2010).

Based on the strength of the existing empirical evidence, treatments are assigned a grade ranging from A to D. Level A treatments are strongly supported by research and have been found to lead to beneficial outcomes among those with traumatic stress reactions. In contrast, Level D treatments lack empirical support and have been found to be ineffective or harmful to those administered such interventions (Foa et al., 2009; Management of Post-Traumatic Stress Working Group, 2010).

Interventions for PTSD are typically organized around phases of recovery: early interventions for acute traumatic stress reactions and prevention of PTSD (reactions that occur from 1 day to less than 1 month after trauma exposure), interventions for acute PTSD (symptom duration of 1 month to fewer than 3 months), and interventions for chronic PTSD (symptom duration of 3 months or longer; Foa et al., 2009). Following is a brief description of these interventions grouped by phases of recovery.

EARLY INTERVENTIONS FOR ACUTE STRESS REACTIONS OR ACUTE STRESS DISORDER

During the early phases of recovery from exposure to a traumatic event, a critical task is the establishment of safety and reduction of psychological distress among those traumatized. Historically, the administration of interventions, such as psychological debriefing

(PD) to groups of individuals immediately following exposure to traumatic events, was mandatory and routine (Bisson, McFarlane, Rose, Ruzek, & Watson, 2009).

Psychological Debriefing

PD typically consisted of one session that provided education on normal reactions to traumatic events, emotional processing of trauma-related reactions, and preparing the individual for possible future trauma-related reactions. Several systematic and meta-analytic reviews conducted on the efficacy of PD, however, have found that it is not effective in reducing psychological distress immediately after trauma or in preventing PTSD (Bisson et al., 2009). Thus, treatment guidelines now recommend *against* the routine use of a single PD session immediately following trauma exposure.

An innate recovery process is believed to be activated after exposure to traumatic events and thus should not be disrupted (Briere & Scott, 2012). Mandatory formal interventions are thus not recommended during this early phase. Instead, the adoption of a "wait and see" approach is suggested. During this early period, client needs and concerns should be assessed to determine whether psychological support or intervention is necessary, and utilization of said support should be voluntary (Bisson et al., 2009).

Support may take the form of ensuring basic physical needs (e.g., shelter, food, sleep, medical care) or psychological needs (e.g., emotional, social, and spiritual) are met and providing relevant information as needed (Bisson et al., 2009; Management of Post-Traumatic Stress Working Group, 2010). For individuals who meet the diagnostic criteria for acute stress disorder and/ or whose posttrauma reactions persist beyond 2 weeks, several treatment guidelines recommend the provision of brief (four to five sessions) cognitive–behavioral interventions, such as exposure-based therapies and cognitive restructuring (described hereafter).

TREATMENT OF ACUTE AND CHRONIC PTSD

For traumatized individuals who meet diagnostic criteria for acute PTSD (symptoms are present for at least 1 month and fewer than 3 months), interventions center on reducing or eliminating PTSD symptoms and preventing chronicity of symptomatology. PTSD is considered chronic when the duration of symptoms extend beyond 3 months. What follows is a review of the most widely used Level A evidence-based treatments for acute and chronic PTSD as recommended by the International Society for Traumatic Stress Studies (ISTSS) PTSD Treatment Guidelines (Foa et al., 2009) and the VA/DoD Clinical Practice Guideline for the Management of Post-Traumatic Stress (Management of Post-Traumatic Stress Working Group, 2010). Most of the treatment interventions described in the following are cognitive behavioral therapy (CBT) approaches that examine how problematic thoughts and behaviors contribute to the development of psychological difficulties (Beck, 2011). Cognitive treatment strategies typically entail the identification and modification of maladaptive thoughts and beliefs that negatively influence emotions and behaviors. Behavioral strategies are designed to disrupt patterns of behavioral avoidance by encouraging clients to gradually and repeatedly face situations, thoughts, and memories that are feared or avoided because of their associations with the traumatic event. Likewise, clients are taught other behavioral strategies, such as deep breathing or applied relaxation, in order to reduce their physiological arousal and painful emotions. CBT approaches are typically structured, short-term, and present-focused and are designed to teach clients coping strategies to more effectively deal with their PTSD symptoms.

Prolonged Exposure Therapy

Prolonged exposure therapy is an evidence-based treatment originally developed by Edna Foa, PhD, a professor at the University of Pennsylvania, for adults who have experienced single or multiple traumas and as a result have developed chronic PTSD and associated symptoms, such as depression and guilt. Over the past 20 years, hundreds of studies have demonstrated the efficacy of prolonged exposure therapy in reducing the psychological effects of trauma, firmly establishing this treatment as a gold-standard Level A treatment in the mental health field (Cahill et al., 2009; Management of Post-Traumatic Stress Working Group, 2010).

Emotional Processing Theory. Prolonged exposure therapy is based on the emotional processing theory (EPT) of anxiety disorders (Foa & Kozak, 1986), which grew out of Lang's (1979) bio-informational theory of emotion and Rachman's (1980) emotional processing theory. According to EPT, fear is organized and stored in memory as cognitive structures that are activated when there are signs of danger. These fear structures may be normal or pathological. The activation of a fear structure triggers physiological responses, cognitive appraisals, and behaviors designed to increase an individual's chances of survival. For example, if you are walking in the woods and a snake emerges from the bushes, a fear structure is activated that contains information about snakes (the fear stimuli), distinct physiological responses to the snake (e.g., immobility, sweating, increased heart rate and blood pressure), the meanings assigned to the snake (e.g., "snakes are dangerous and will harm me"), and the interpretation of one's physiological responses (e.g., "my heart is racing so I must be afraid").

Fear structures are considered normal or adaptive when the threats in one's environment are realistic, because it propels the individual to take appropriate action to avoid or escape danger. In the case of the snake, an adaptive fear response may include backing away slowly and walking in a different direction or scaring the snake away with stick. According to EPT, anxiety disorders develop when normal fear structures become pathological.

When Fear Structures Become Pathological. Foa and Kozak (1986) proposed that normal fear structures become pathological due to several related processes: (1) safe or harmless stimuli are perceived as dangerous, (2) which in turn activates physiological and behavioral responses that are inappropriate given the context, and (3) these response elements are presumed to be excessive and maladaptive, and (4) the meanings associated with these stimuli and responses are mistakenly associated with threat. Treatment of anxiety disorders thus involves modification of these pathological fear structures and the development of adaptive fear structures that compete with maladaptive ones.

Emotional Processing Theory and Chronic PTSD. Emotional processing theory has since been elaborated upon to account for the development and treatment of chronic PTSD (Foa, Huppert, & Cahill, 2006; Rauch & Foa, 2006). In particular, EPT proposes that following a traumatic event, a fear network is formed that stores information about sources of threat. Such networks are characterized by multiple stimulus and response elements that are closely interrelated due to their strong association with fear. Thus, stimuli present during the trauma become associated with the perception of threat and thus activate the fear structure, which in turn leads to escape or avoidance behaviors. Individuals who develop PTSD come to view the world as a dangerous and unsafe place. Furthermore, the traumatized individual stores negative representations of how they responded during the traumatic event and their subsequent symptoms of PTSD. Two key beliefs are presumed to be at play in maintaining PTSD symptoms: "The world is entirely dangerous," and "I am completely incompetent."

Individuals with PTSD also tend to have trauma memories that are disorganized or fragmented because they were encoded under conditions of extreme stress (Foa et al., 2006). The development of chronic PTSD is presumed to be a function of the individual's difficulty with adequately processing his or her trauma memories and his or her avoidance of thoughts, feelings, or situations that remind him or her of the trauma. While this strategy works in the short run—through the process of negative reinforcement—to reduce anxiety, in the long run it serves to maintain the PTSD symptoms and interferes with the individual's functioning.

Emotional processing theory argues that a key mechanism of effective psychosocial interventions for PTSD includes emotional processing of the trauma memories, modification of the pathological elements of the fear structure, or development of a new structure that competes with the fear structure (Foa & Kozak, 1986; Foa et al., 2006; Rauch & Foa, 2006). Pathological fear structures are modified in several ways. First, the fear structure is activated through a process whereby individuals with PTSD directly confront their trauma-related thoughts, feelings, and situations. Second, through exposing themselves to their fears, clients with PTSD learn that their beliefs about themselves and the world are not true (i.e., they learn that the world is not always a dangerous place and that their beliefs are exaggerated).

Treatment Elements. Prolonged exposure therapy is typically administered over a period of 10 to 15 sessions, each lasting for 90 minutes, and consists of several components: (1) breathing retraining, (2) psychoeducation about common reactions to trauma and PTSD, (3) in vivo exposures (i.e., the client repeatedly and gradually confronts or faces activities and situations that are feared and avoided because of the trauma), and (4) imaginal exposures (i.e., the client repeatedly describes the traumatic event[s] in detail with the therapist until the fear associated with the memories subsides; Foa, Hembree, & Rothbaum, 2007). What follows is a brief overview of the treatment protocol as described in the manual *Prolonged Exposure Therapy for PTSD: Emotional Processing of Traumatic Experiences, Therapist Guide* (Foa et al., 2007).

During the first session, the clients are provided with a strong rationale for utilization of prolonged exposure techniques and tools (i.e., imaginal and in vivo exposures), based on emotional processing theory, which lays the groundwork for future sessions. Clients are then introduced to breathing retraining, which provides a specific tool they can use during the upcoming weeks. Clients are educated about how the breathing process becomes disrupted during episodes of fear: Instead of breathing normally, people begin to hyperventilate (breathe more quickly than needed), which signals to the body that it needs to prepare for danger, which in turn triggers additional physiological responses. The disruptions in breathing and the client's interpretation of their bodily reactions further add to the feelings of fear.

The purpose of breathing retraining is to slow down the breathing process, which helps to reduce feelings of anxiety and stress and increase feelings of calm and relaxation. Clients are taught how to slow down their breathing and to pair their slow breathing with a relaxing word such as "calm" or "relax." Clients are advised to practice three times a day, for 10 minutes each time.

In the second session, clients are provided with psychoeducation about the nature of trauma and typical reactions to trauma. During this conversation, clients are encouraged to discuss their own personal experiences with trauma and the ways in which their PTSD symptoms have affected their lives. This process allows for the normalization and validation of the client's experiences. And the client comes to understand that his or her reactions are understandable given the nature of the trauma he or she experienced. Moreover, the discussion of trauma provides an opportunity to instill hope in the client that with support and treatment, his or her PTSD symptoms can be significantly reduced or improved. During this session, the client is also provided a rationale for in vivo exposures (i.e., the process of gradually facing trauma-related activities and situations that are avoided) to facilitate understanding of the importance of this strategy in recovering from PTSD.

In collaboration with the therapist, the client constructs a hierarchy of feared situations that are avoided, which are organized from least to most distressing. The client is then assigned the task of confronting a feared situation from his or her list. For example, a traumatized client may avoid going to parks because that was where he or she was assaulted. Through repeated in vivo exposures, the client gradually learns to face his or her fear of parks and eventually go to a park without experiencing undue anxiety.

During the third session, the client is provided with a rationale for the utilization of imaginal exposures. Imaginal exposure consists of having the client repeatedly recount the trauma experience or memory as vividly as possible in the present tense. This provides an opportunity for the client to emotionally engage with and process the trauma memory. Through repeated imaginal exposures to the memories, the client comes to learn that the trauma memories are not dangerous, that the experience was in the past and is not happening again in the present, and that he or she can gain control over the trauma memories and make sense of them. Over the course of several retellings of the trauma experience, the trauma memories become more organized and the client also experiences a lessening of the emotional distress (also known as habituation) associated with the trauma memories. In general, trauma memories are confronted gradually, and the client is given full control over the pace at which he or she recounts details of the trauma.

Subsequent prolonged exposure sessions (sessions 4 to 9) consist of conducting additional imaginal exposures, processing the imaginal exposures, and reviewing the client's experience with their in vivo exposures outside of the session. During the final session, the client and the therapist review the progress that the client has made and the skills that he or she has learned to date. Throughout the course of treatment, clients are instructed to monitor their trauma-related symptoms on a weekly basis using self-report measures, which provides feedback to the client and therapist about changes in the client's symptomatology and about progress made in treatment.

While prolonged exposure has had tremendous success among people with trauma histories and PTSD, it is not recommended for everyone. Prolonged exposure is contraindicated for individuals who are at high risk for suicidal, homicidal, or self-injurious behaviors. Individuals with current psychosis who have a high risk of being assaulted (e.g., those in current domestic violence situations) are also excluded. These behaviors and experiences require immediate attention and stabilization before trauma work can begin. A general consensus is that safety should take priority over treatment. Likewise, due to the difficulty of accessing and processing the trauma memories, individuals who do not have a clear memory, or who have an insufficient memory, of the traumatic event are excluded.

Despite evidence supporting prolonged exposure's efficacy with PTSD, some clinicians remain reluctant to utilize this treatment, fearing that it will be too overwhelming for the clients and may lead to harmful effects for both clients and clinicians (Olatunji, Deacon, & Abramowitz, 2009). Negative beliefs and emotions about the implementation of prolonged exposure, along with inadequate training, set the stage for challenges in the widespread implementation of this treatment method. However, large-scale training initiatives are in place, particularly within the VA system, to systematically train and provide supervision for the successful implementation of prolonged exposure among veteran/military populations with PTSD (Rauch, Eftekhari, & Ruzek, 2012).

Olatunji et al. (2009) suggest creating a therapeutic context in which informed consent is continually obtained throughout the course of treatment before the implementation of any exposure procedures with an eye to anticipating and planning for the management of any negative outcomes. Through the use of continued education and collaborative planning with the client, risks can be minimized and prolonged exposure safely implemented.

Cognitive Processing Therapy

Cognitive processing therapy (CPT), a form of CBT for PTSD that incorporates components of exposure therapy, was originally developed by Patricia Resick and Monica Schnicke for the treatment of rape victims (Resick, & Schnicke, 1993). More recently, CPT has been modified for use with veteran and military populations

(Resick, Monson, & Chard, 2007). Along with prolonged exposure, CPT has been chosen as a gold-standard treatment for dissemination and training among all military treatment providers (Chard, Ricksecker, Healy, Karlin, & Resick, 2012).

CPT is based on social cognitive theory, which proposes that how a person interprets a traumatic event determines his or her emotional reactions to the events. Prior to experiencing a traumatic event, individuals have either positive or negative beliefs about themselves, others, and the world that developed out of important developmental experiences. A common belief held by many individuals is the "just world belief," which states that "good things happen to good people and bad things happen to bad people."

Traumatic events are presumed to alter or disrupt individuals' core beliefs about themselves and the world. When an individual experiences an unexpected traumatic event that does not fit with prior beliefs, the individual then attempts to integrate the traumatic experience into his or her belief system in order to reconcile the experience through one of several cognitive processes: assimilation, accommodation, or overaccommodation (Resick et al., 2007).

Assimilation occurs when the individual alters his or her memories of the traumatic event or interpretation of the event in order to fit with his or her current beliefs or to preserve preexisting beliefs. The individual may blame himself or herself for the traumatic event (e.g., "If only I had not done [*a certain behavior*] then maybe [*the traumatic event*] would not have happened," or "I must have done something wrong to deserve this"). He or she may have trouble accepting that the event happened and so may deny the event happened (e.g., "Maybe [*the traumatic event*] didn't happen") or forget the most terrifying parts of the trauma. These responses may be perceived as the easiest way for the individual to preserve his or her belief in a just world and in his or her ability to keep himself or herself safe.

Accommodation occurs when the individual changes his or her beliefs in order to integrate and accept the experience of the trauma (e.g., "I wasn't able to fight back at the time," or "Bad things happen to good people," or "Although I wasn't able to use good judgment in that situation, most of the time I make good decisions"). Accommodation is considered a healthy response and is one of the main outcome goals of CPT.

Overaccommodation occurs when the individual alters his or her prior beliefs about himself or herself and the world in an extreme way (e.g., "I'll never be safe," "I can't trust my judgment," or "No one can be trusted"), which further contributes to feelings of fear and to difficulty developing trust and intimacy in relationships.

For some individuals who hold preexisting negative beliefs about themselves and the world, new exposures to traumatic events further reinforce or confirm these previously held beliefs (e.g., if a client was previously betrayed by a family member or someone close to him or her, then he or she may have developed the overgeneralized belief "I can't trust anyone"). When this particular client experiences another interpersonal trauma, that new event serves to reinforce mistrust of others.

The goals of CPT include helping the traumatized client to develop more balanced and realistic views about himself or herself and others through activation and correction of faulty beliefs about the trauma, helping the client to accept that the traumatic event occurred and to experience the emotions associated with the trauma instead of denying them.

Treatment Elements. CPT is usually administered over the course of 12 sessions and consists of several components: (1) psychoeducation, (2) written accounts of the traumatic memory, and (3) cognitive restructuring. What follows is a brief overview of the treatment as described in the manual *Cognitive Processing Therapy Veteran/Military Version* (Resick et al., 2007). Session 1 provides the client with education about the nature of trauma and the symptoms of PTSD and depression and provides a rationale for the treatment based on the cognitive conceptualization of PTSD. This includes how trauma can change an individual's belief system in various ways (e.g., via assimilation, accommodation, or overaccommodation), how through the identification and modification of negative thoughts about the traumatic events (stuck points) the client can recover from the distress, and the distinction between natural versus manufactured emotions (the latter being a consequence of stuck points).

At the end of session 1, the client is assigned homework: writing about the impact of the trauma on his or her life in the areas of safety, trust, power and control, esteem, and intimacy (i.e., the impact statement). During session 2, the client reads the impact statement and with the therapist's help begins the process of identifying stuck points related to the trauma. Additionally, the therapist teaches the client basic cognitive restructuring techniques including learning about the connection between activating events (A), thoughts/beliefs (B), and feelings (C). Homework assignment entails daily completion of ABC worksheets.

Session 3 continues the process of teaching the client cognitive restructuring techniques and includes further discussions using the ABC worksheets as they relate to the traumatic event and challenging stuck points related to the trauma. At the end of this session, the client is assigned the task of writing an account of his or her trauma experience that includes sensory details, thoughts, and feelings that occurred during the traumatic event. The client is asked to read the written trauma account and complete ABC worksheets on a daily basis.

During session 4, the client reads his or her written trauma account and is encouraged to access and express the emotions associated with the trauma. During this process the therapist remains alert for client stuck points about the traumatic events and, through the use of open-ended questions, begins the process of challenging the client's self-blame, guilt, or other overgeneralized beliefs that she or he may hold related to the traumatic event. Through the use of questioning, the therapist helps the client to contextualize the traumatic event and to realize that behaviors enacted during the traumatic event were understandable in light of the context in which they occurred.

With this method, the therapist helps the client reduce feelings of self-blame and guilt by helping him or her see that the traumatic event was not his or her fault—that he or she could not have prevented it. At the end of this session, the client is assigned the task of writing the trauma account again but this time is encouraged to also write about how he or she is thinking and feeling about the process of writing the trauma account. After rewriting the trauma account, the client continues to read the trauma account and complete ABC worksheets on a daily basis.

During sessions 5 to 7, key cognitive restructuring techniques are continued, such as learning questions to challenge stuck points (i.e., dysfunctional assimilated or overaccommodated beliefs), identifying faulty patterns of thinking (stuck points), and learning how to generate new and more adaptive beliefs about self, others, and the world in relation to the trauma experience. Sessions 8 to 12 focus on specific domains that may have been negatively impacted by the traumatic event, such as safety, trust, power and control, esteem, and intimacy.

Each module begins with education on how trauma may have affected a specific domain. Through the use of challenging beliefs worksheets, the therapist helps the client to challenge stuck points (i.e., negative or problematic thoughts) related to that particular domain and gain a more balanced perspective about that area of life. In the final session, the client rewrites the impact statement and then reads it again, reflecting on ways in which the statement has changed.

CPT is recognized as a Level A PTSD treatment by both the ISTSS (Foa et al., 2009) and VA/DoD (Management of Post-Traumatic Stress Working Group, 2010) treatment guidelines. To date, six empirical studies (four randomized controlled trials and two nonrandomized trials) have found CPT to be efficacious in the reduction of PTSD symptoms and associated guilt and shame. Of note, however, is a dismantling study designed to better understand which components of CPT were most effective in influencing treatment outcomes (Resick et al., 2008).

One hundred fifty women who developed PTSD as a consequence of interpersonal violence were randomly assigned to one of three treatment conditions: the full CPT protocol (as described previously), CPT-Cognitive Only (CPT-C; this protocol was similar to the full protocol but written accounts were removed), or written accounts (WA; this protocol consisted of two educational sessions reviewing the nature of trauma reactions and utilizing the Subjective Units of Distress [SUDs] scale; the remaining sessions were devoted to clients' writing about their traumatic events and reading their trauma accounts to the therapist, something they did both during and between sessions). Although all three conditions led to clinically significant reductions in PTSD, further examination of the results revealed some interesting findings: (1) There were no significant differences between the full CPT protocol and the CPT-C treatment condition, suggesting comparable effectiveness, and (2) CPT-C outperformed WA in achieving significant PTSD reductions. The researchers thus concluded that WA was not a necessary component for all clients. Thus clinicians have the option of administering CPT without WA (Chard et al., 2012). Nevertheless, for clients who could benefit from fully accessing and emotionally processing their traumatic memories, the original CPT protocol can be administered in its entirety.

Eye Movement Desensitization and Reprocessing

Eye movement desensitization and reprocessing (EMDR) therapy was originally developed by Francine Shapiro in 1989 when she noticed the effects of eye movements on reducing the intensity of negative emotions. EMDR is a treatment modality that incorporates several theoretical perspectives, including cognitive–behavioral, psychodynamic, interactional, and body-based perspectives (Shapiro & Maxfield, 2002). EMDR is based on the theory of adaptive information processing (AIP), which proposes that PTSD and associated negative reactions are a function of unprocessed distressing memories.

The goal of EMDR is to assist clients in accessing and processing their traumatic memories in service of coming to an adaptive resolution (Shapiro, 2001). The presumed mechanism of EMDR lies in the enhanced information processing that occurs as a result of saccadic eye movements. Eye movements are assumed to be useful because they reduce the vividness of the trauma images and their associated distressing emotions. Desensitization eventually occurs, which leads to a reduction in distress and avoidance of the memories (Shapiro & Maxfield, 2002).

Treatment Elements. The treatment elements of EMDR comprise eight stages: (1) history and treatment planning, (2) preparation, (3) assessment of trauma, (4) desensitization and reprocessing, (5) installation of positive cognitions, (6) body scan, (7) closure, and (8) reevaluation. Phases 3 through 8 are procedures that are repeated throughout the treatment. Depending on the level of severity of PTSD symptoms and client needs and preferences, session frequency may range from a few sessions to several months. What follows is a brief overview of the treatment as described in the text *Eye Movement and Reprocessing: Basic Principles, Protocols, and Procedures* (Shapiro, 2001).

During phase 1, a *complete history* of the client's background and symptom profile is gathered while also ascertaining the client's readiness to begin EMDR. Additionally, a *treatment plan* is developed that incorporates key goals and targets for treatment including development of coping skills and processing of trauma memories.

During *preparation*, the clinician provides the client with education regarding the nature of the trauma, the specific treatment procedures and their rationale are reviewed in detail, and strategies for coping with trauma reactions are taught to the client (e.g., relaxation strategies, affect regulation, and self-control strategies). Since many individuals with trauma histories have difficulties with affect regulation, impulse control, and avoidance, a key goal during this phase is to stabilize the client and prepare him or her for the ensuing trauma work.

Assessment entails gathering information about the specific trauma memory that will be focused on including any associated negative beliefs (e.g., "I'm unlovable") and emotions. Clients are then asked to identify an alternative positive belief (e.g., "I'm lovable"), and rate the validity of that belief on a scale of 0 (not valid at all) to 7 (completely valid). Trauma-related emotions and physical sensations and bodily locations are also elicited from the client.

The key phase of EMDR, *desensitization and reprocessing*, entails asking the client to hold the distressing trauma images, bodily sensations, and negative beliefs in mind as the therapist moves his or her fingers in a rhythmic fashion across the client's complete visual field. The client is asked to follow the therapist's fingers for about 20 seconds, after which he or she is asked to let go of the trauma images and to take a deep breath. Feedback is elicited from the client about any changes that may have occurred in his or her trauma images, sensations, thoughts, or emotions. During the next set of eye movements, the client is asked to focus on the changes or new associations that have occurred since the prior episode of eye movements. The authors note that other dual-attention stimuli (e.g., hand tapping or tones) can be utilized instead of eye movements.

The *installation of positive cognitions* phase begins after the client is desensitized to their trauma images or memories. Level of desensitization to the trauma memory is ascertained by reviewing the client's subjective units of distress (SUDs), ranging from 0 (no distress) to 10 (very distressing). When the client's SUDs related to the trauma memory is at a 0 or 1, she or he is asked to hold the new positive belief in mind while visually tracking the therapist's fingers. The client is then asked to report on changes in her or his perception of the validity of the positive belief on a scale of 1 (not valid at all) to 7 (completely valid).

During the *body scan* phase, the client is asked to attend to any remaining bodily discomforts and tensions. Negative trauma images that are stored in memory are often associated with physiological sensations. Thus EMDR is presumed to be incomplete if the client is not able to access the trauma memories without accompanying physical sensations. Clients are then asked to focus on those specific physical areas as they track the therapist's fingers until the physical tension subsides.

During the *closure* phase, the client is taught standard coping skills, such as relaxation training or positive visualization, to deal with distressing images or memories that may emerge in the upcoming days. Furthermore, clients are encouraged to keep a journal in which they can document their thoughts and emotions related to the trauma as needed.

Finally, at the beginning of each session after the evaluation, a *reevaluation process* occurs whereby the therapist and client review the treatment goals to determine whether the trauma memories have been fully processed and any gains maintained. Client journal entries are reviewed to identify additional issues that need to be addressed or new coping skills that need to be learned (Shapiro, 2001; Shapiro & Maxfield, 2002).

A recent review of seven meta-analyses of EMDR found it to be an efficacious treatment for PTSD and as effective as traditional exposure-based interventions (Spates, Koch, Cusack, Pagoto, & Waller, 2008), garnering the intervention a Level A rating from both the ISTSS (Foa et al., 2009) and the VA/DoD treatment guidelines (Management of Post-Traumatic Stress Working Group, 2010). One controversy that remains regarding this treatment, however, is whether the eye movements utilized in EMDR are necessary to obtain reductions in PTSD. Several dismantling studies have been conducted and found no convincing evidence that eye movements are necessary in reducing PTSD, suggesting EMDR's mechanism of action may be similar to other exposure therapies (i.e., cognitive and emotional processing of the trauma memories and images). Thus EMDR could be administered without the eye movements, as this procedure would not influence treatment outcomes above and beyond the exposure component (Spates et al., 2008).

More recently, Schubert, Lee, and Drummond (2011) conducted a study with 62 participants with negative trauma memories who received a single session of EMDR without eye movements or a single session of EMDR with either fixed or variable rates of eye movements. The researchers found that the eye movement component had distinct beneficial effects, including reductions in heart rate and skin conductance, which aided in the processing of negative trauma memories, suggesting further research is necessary to clarify the function of the eye movements (Schubert et al., 2011). Some researchers argue that the eye movements may serve as an additional form of distraction that helps the client focus on the distressing trauma images and memories during treatment (Spates et al., 2008).

Stress Inoculation Treatment

Stress inoculation treatment (SIT) was originally developed by Donald Meichenbaum (1985, 1996) as a treatment for anxiety disorders and was later modified for the treatment of rape-induced PTSD. SIT is based on a transactional view of stress that proposes a bidirectional relationship between the individual and the environment. When stressful events are perceived as exceeding an individual's coping capacities, then anxiety develops as a result (Meichenbaum, 2008). In tandem, this treatment model ascribes to a constructivist narrative perspective (CNP), which proposes that the narratives that clients construct to make sense of their experiences play an important role in their capacity to manage stress.

Treatment Elements. SIT for PTSD consists of three phases: (1) education, (2) skill acquisition and consolidation, and (3) application. During the education phase, clients are taught generally about the interactional nature of stress, particularly about trauma-related stress reactions. During the skill acquisition and consolidation phase, clients are taught several interrelated behavioral (e.g., problem solving and assertiveness training), emotional (relaxation training, breathing retraining), and cognitive (e.g., self-talk, thought stopping) coping strategies to help them manage and reduce trauma-related anxiety. With sufficient reduction in anxiety, there is an associated decrease in avoidance behaviors and improvements in PTSD symptoms. Finally, during the application phase, clients are encouraged to apply the skills they have learned to real-life situations.

While SIT is not considered a trauma-focused psychotherapy per se, it has nevertheless garnered sufficient empirical support to rank it as a first-line treatment for PTSD (Foa et al., 2009; Management of Post-Traumatic Stress Working Group, 2010). To date, eight studies (four of which were randomized controlled trials) have found SIT to be as effective as traditional trauma-focused psychotherapies (e.g., CBT and EMDR) in reducing symptoms of PTSD (Cahill et al., 2009). Based on the findings of two randomized controlled trials with female sexual assault survivors (Foa et al., 1999; Foa, Rothbaum, Riggs, & Murdock, 1991), SIT was given a Level A rating from both ISTSS (Foa et al., 2009) and the VA/DoD Clinical Practice Guidelines (Management of Post-Traumatic Stress Working Group, 2010).

Pharmacotherapy for PTSD

The rationale for the use of pharmacotherapy as a first-line treatment for PTSD stems from several key findings related to the neurobiological changes associated with PTSD. Studies indicate that PTSD is associated with disruptions in the neurotransmitter, neuroendocrine, and neurohormonal systems (Friedman, Davidson, & Stein, 2009; Stein, Ipser, & Seedat, 2006; Sullivan & Neria, 2009). Individuals with PTSD tend to have a dysregulated hypothalamic–pituitary–adrenal (HPA) axis, which plays a key role in the regulation of the stress response.

Individuals with PTSD also have inadequate serotonergic, dopaminergic, and GABA-ergic functions, all of which are associated with the symptom clusters of PTSD (re-experiencing, avoidance/numbing, and hyperarousal symptoms). PTSD is also associated with specific structural and functional brain abnormalities (Sullivan & Neria, 2009). Many of these biological changes or dysfunctions may benefit from medication intervention. Finally, PTSD is often comorbid with other psychiatric conditions (e.g., depression and other anxiety disorders) that are known to respond to pharmacotherapy interventions, thus providing further support for the use of medications in treating PTSD (Friedman et al., 2009). Since pharmacotherapy is a treatment that is accessible to many, is widely accepted by clients, and may be preferred to psychotherapy by some clients, it is often seen as an alternative or adjunct to psychotherapy interventions.

Several recent reviews have been conducted to answer the question of whether established pharmacotherapies (i.e., antidepressants and anxiolytics) are effective in treating PTSD and if so, whether certain medication classes are more effective than others. Stein et al. (2006) conducted a review of 35 randomized controlled trials of short-term medication treatments for PTSD and found that medications were significantly more effective than placebo in reducing PTSD symptoms severity, and approximately 60% of those receiving medications showed a treatment response compared to only 38% of those receiving placebo.

In terms of medication classes, the selective serotonin reuptake inhibitors (SSRIs; e.g., sertraline, paroxetine, and fluoxetine) were found to have the most convincing evidence for treatment efficacy. A later review by Friedman et al. (2009) found that both SSRIs and serotonin–norepinephrine reuptake inhibitors (SNRIs; e.g., venlafaxine-extended release) were significantly associated with reductions in PTSD and were thus recommended as first-line treatments. Benefits of medication treatments for PTSD were found for both short-term treatments and long-term maintenance treatments.

Overall, pharmacotherapies such as SSRIs and SNRIs appear be well tolerated by those with PTSD and promote global improvements across symptom and life spheres (Friedman et al., 2009; Sullivan & Neria, 2009). To date, two SSRIs, sertraline (Zoloft) and paroxetine (Paxil), have been FDA-approved for the treatment of PTSD because they have the strongest empirical support (Jeffreys, Capehart, & Friedman, 2012). There is no evidence to support the use of atypical antipsychotic or anti-anxiety medications for adjunctive treatment of PTSD (Jeffreys et al., 2012). When considering the utilization of pharmacotherapies in the treatment of PTSD, clients should be referred for a psychiatric evaluation for a medication consultation. It is generally recommended that pharmacotherapy be offered in conjunction with first-line trauma-focused psychotherapies (Jeffreys, Capehart, & Friedman, 2012; Sullivan & Neria, 2009).

Sleep Interventions

Sleep disturbances are common in trauma survivors. They can exacerbate depression and PTSD, increase symptomatology, and have a negative effect on health. Trauma-related sleep disorders had an independent effect on health in a sample of female sexual-assault survivors, even after controlling for both depression and PTSD (Clum et al., 2001). Sleep problems can make everyday life more difficult. Poor sleep means greater daytime fatigue, more concentration and memory impairments, poorer academic performance, and more accidents (Bronstein & Montgomery, 2013).

Spoormaker and Montgomery (2008) argue that sleep is not a secondary disorder to PTSD but is in fact a core issue. Poor sleep is a risk factor for PTSD and often precedes it. In addition, poor sleep is a frequent residual complaint following treatment. Moreover, treating sleep disorders alleviates both sleep disturbances and PTSD. But treating PTSD alone often fails to treat the sleep problems. The sleep abnormalities found in polysomnographic studies showed more stage 1 sleep, less slow-wave sleep, and higher REM density. REM sleep is initiated by cholinergic nuclei in the brainstem and characterized by increased acetylcholine activity. It is terminated with norepinephrine activity increases. The amygdala has a role in REM sleep and is related to the actions of acetylcholine and norepinephrine. Nightmares seem directly related to high norepinephrine levels in people with PTSD.

The types of sleep problems that are common in trauma survivors include longer sleep latency (minutes to get to sleep), more trouble staying asleep, more nightmares, and less sleep overall. This can be seen in various samples of trauma survivors where sleep is measured. For example, a sample of Afghan refugee children, aged 13 to 18, had greater length of sleep latency overall—on average 20 minutes longer than normative groups (Bronstein & Montgomery, 2013). Many of these children had been exposed to extreme violence, terror, physical or sexual abuse, and rape. Children who were above the cutoff for PTSD took significantly more minutes to fall asleep (greater sleep onset latency) and had more nightmares and less total sleep than the refugee children who did not have PTSD.

In one recent study, sleep disturbances were one of the most commonly occurring presenting problems in a treatment for veterans with PTSD (Rosen, Adler, & Tiet, 2013). Sleep problems slow recovery from PTSD, increase reactivity to social cues, and compromise both social and occupational functioning (Nappi, Drummond, & Hall, 2012). More concerning, sleep problems were a better predictor of suicidal ideation and behavior than either depression or hopelessness in a sample of young adults in the military who had been referred for severe suicidality ($N = 311$; Ribeiro et al., 2012). The importance of sleep may be due to the hyperarousal associated with PTSD, which may be necessary in order to override the survival instinct. Insomnia could be just one manifestation of the overaroused state. Insomnia can also impair decision making. The sleep problems that appear to elevate the risk for suicide include insomnia, poor sleep quality, and nightmares. The authors of this study concluded that insomnia is an important target for suicide risk assessment and that treating insomnia may help prevent suicide in this vulnerable population.

There was a similar finding in a study comparing patients with suicidal ideation ($N = 211$) with patients with no suicidal ideation ($N = 1,373$) who were presenting at a community-based sleep medical center (Krakow, Ribeiro, Ulibarri, Krakow, & Joiner, 2011). In this study, the patients with suicidal ideation had significantly more sleep problems, including insomnia, nightmares, poor sleep quality, and sleep-related impairment and quality of life. Suicidal ideation was consistently related to a range of sleep complaints, even after controlling for depressive symptoms. Some of the severe symptoms that were related to suicidal ideation include "acting out dreams," making disruptive noises during sleep, time monitoring behavior, "losing sleep over losing sleep," and failing to create a positive sleep environment. The suicidal ideation group also showed longer sleep onset latency and longer time in bed, with lower sleep efficacy scores (total time in bed versus total time sleeping). They had poorer subjective sleep and reported more daytime fatigue, which affected their daytime functioning. They also reported lower quality of life than the non–suicidal ideation group. Fortunately, sleep problems are often distressing enough to encourage patients who might otherwise avoid treatment to seek help (Nappi et al., 2012).

Assessment of Sleep Disorders

The term "sleep disorders" covers a wide range of problems. Some disorders are measured by asking patients about them via patient questionnaire, including about such things as length of time to get to sleep and frequency of nightmares. Other sleep parameters need to be measured with polysomnograph. A polysomnograph records vital signs and other physiological measures during sleep. A polysomnographic study includes an EEG (electroencephalogram) to measure brain wave activity, an EMG (electromyogram) to measure muscle activity, and an EOG (electro-oculogram) to measure eye movements. Other measures include respiratory airflow, blood oxygen saturation, pulse, heart rate, body position, and respiratory effort. Polysomnographic studies are necessary to detect problems that cannot be detected by patient questionnaire alone, often because patients are unaware they have them. These disorders include sleep-disordered breathing (e.g., sleep apneas), and sleep-movement disorders (e.g., restless legs syndrome).

Morin and Ware (1996) recommended that clinicians include a systematic assessment of sleep in all psychological evaluations. They suggest that practitioners note when the sleep disorder started and the temporal sequence of the onset of the sleep disorder and the onset of the psychiatric disorder. Did the symptoms of the psychiatric disorder predate the onset of sleep problems or vice versa? Polysomnographic studies can also reveal whether there are any sleep–breathing or sleep–movement disorders that might also be treated. These conditions often improve with medications and/or assistive devices.

Cognitive-Behavioral Approaches for Sleep Problems

CBT for sleep problems in the general population effectively treats sleep problems. In one review, it was effective for 70% to 80% of patients and was comparable to sleep medications (Morin, 2004; Stepanski & Perlis, 2000). Cognitive approaches can also address worrying and rumination that may be at the base of primary or secondary insomnia (Morin & Ware, 1996). Cognitive therapy for insomnia includes behavioral, cognitive, and educational components.

- Behavioral aspects include establishing regular bedtimes, not using the bed for anything but sleeping and sex, getting out of bed when unable to sleep, and eliminating naps during the day.
- Sleep hygiene education helps people minimize behaviors that might interfere with sleep. This might include eliminating caffeine, exercise, alcohol, and smoking too close to bedtime (Morin, 2004; Stepanski & Perlis, 2000).
- Stress reduction includes a relaxation component that focuses on both autonomic relaxation techniques (e.g., progressive muscle relaxation) and cognitive techniques that address the worrying that keeps people from sleeping. A combination of cognitive, behavioral, and stress-reduction approaches is effective for most patients with sleep disorders.

However, cognitive therapy alone may not be enough to effectively deal with all the sleep problems associated with PTSD. In one recent study, 55 patients with PTSD participated in a cognitive–behavioral intervention to improve their sleep (Belleville, Guay, & Marchand, 2009). The intervention included psychoeducation about PTSD, anxiety management techniques, cognitive restructuring, prolonged exposure, and relapse prevention for an average of 19 sessions. At the conclusion of treatment, there were significant improvements in many of the sleep parameters: sleep quality, sleep onset latency, sleep efficiency, and sleep disturbances. But these changes were not maintained after 6 months. Furthermore, 70% of the patients who initially had sleep problems still had sleep problems after treatment. People with severe PTSD were more likely to have sleep problems, as well as depression, anxiety, and poorer health.

Time-monitoring behavior (or nocturnal "clock watching") is a common behavior among patients with insomnia. It includes both external behaviors (watching the clock) and internal behaviors (ruminations and mental calculations about the amount of time left in a night and the amount of sleep). Time-monitoring behavior leads to frustration about sleeplessness and perpetuates it. This behavior was also common in trauma survivors in a sample of 1,078 patients who presented at a sleep medicine clinic (Krakow, Krakow, Ulibarri, & Krakow, 2012). In this sample, 32% reported moderate to severe posttraumatic stress symptoms. Both insomnia and time monitoring were more common in the patients with posttraumatic stress symptoms. Furthermore, insomnia and time monitoring were more common in those who had more severe posttraumatic stress. The authors noted that simple cognitive therapy and sleep hygiene instructions for patients not to engage in this behavior are effective with those who have mild or moderate posttraumatic stress. However, among those with more severe symptoms, these techniques are not effective, because these behaviors are a coping mechanism for patients with severe posttraumatic stress and severe sleep disorders. The authors state that a different approach is needed for these patients, but that such an approach was beyond the scope of their current investigation.

COGNITIVE–BEHAVIORAL SLEEP APP: CBT-i COACH

The CBT-i Coach is a free mobile application (mobile app) available from the National Center for Posttraumatic Stress Disorder that is designed to help trauma survivors develop good sleep habits and sleep better. This app is designed to be used in conjunction with therapy to help trauma survivors get the most out of their CBT for Insomnia (CBT-i).

Features of this app allow trauma survivors to

- Record daily sleep and track insomnia symptom changes with a sleep diary
- Update sleep prescriptions with provider recommendations
- Use tools and exercises to quiet their mind
- Learn about sleep, the benefits of sleep hygiene, and terms used in CBT-i
- Set reminder messages with tips, motivation, and alarms to change sleep habits

Source: www.ptsd.va.gov/public/pages/cbti-coach-app.asp

Interventions to Reduce Nightmares

Nightmares can be one of the most difficult sleep symptoms to cope with, and they are the most common re-experiencing symptom in PTSD (Escamilla, LaVoy, Moore, & Krakow, 2012). Nightmares are frightening dreams that lead to awakening. They are often related to fear of falling asleep, which influences sleep quality and results in chronic distress. The sleep deprivation that results from chronic nightmares can have a negative effect on memory, creativity, mood, attention, learning, and stress.

Escamilla and colleagues (2012) indicate that sleep problems are also costly: in the United States they account for $16 billion in direct health costs and $50 billion to $100 billion in indirect costs, such as lost productivity and accidents.

Pharmacologic Interventions for Nightmares. The medication prazosin is considered a front-line treatment for posttraumatic nightmares (Escamilla et al., 2012; Nappi et al., 2012). The proposed mechanism for this drug's effectiveness is that it blocks a portion of the adrenaline response. Because of this, it reduces anxiety, improves sleep, and affects REM to reduce nightmares. It is generally well tolerated and does not produce a medication "hangover." When the medication is stopped, the posttraumatic nightmares and insomnia often return.

Risperidone is an atypical antipsychotic that has also shown effectiveness in reducing posttraumatic nightmares. This is an off-label use. Risperidone reduces PTSD symptoms of anxiety and insomnia due to its combined receptor antagonism of dopamine and serotonin. It also has similar properties to the antihypertensive agents (Escamilla et al., 2012). Trazadone is an antidepressant and augmenter drug that helps with sleep-onset insomnia. It is an alpha-adrenergic receptor antagonist and histaminergic antagonist. It increases total sleep time and decreases REM (when nightmare are more likely to occur; Escamilla et al., 2012). However, at least one recent review referred to the evidence for its efficacy for sleep problems in PTSD as "sparse" (Nappi et al., 2012).

All three classes of antidepressants (SSRIs, tricyclics, and monoamine oxidase inhibitors [MAOIs]) have not shown to be effective treatments for PTSD-related insomnia and nightmares. Similarly, there is limited support for the use of benzodiazepines or nonbenzodiazepines, such as zolpidem, as treatments for PTSD-related sleep problems (Nappi et al., 2012).

Cognitive–Behavioral Approaches to Posttraumatic Nightmares. The most effective nonpharmacologic interventions for nightmares are the cognitive–behavioral approaches (Escamilla et al., 2012). The most common of these approaches is imagery rehearsal therapy (IRT). IRT involves basic sleep hygiene training, trauma education, or identifying themes in the nightmares

(Hansen, Hofling, Kroner-Borowik, Stangier, & Steil, 2013). It has proven to be a highly effective treatment for posttraumatic nightmares (Escamilla et al., 2012), although some recent studies have found that it is most effective when used in conjunction with CBT.

A related technique is exposure, relaxation, and rescripting therapy (ERRT). ERRT is another short-term technique. It includes relaxation training; education about trauma, PTSD, nightmares, and sleep hygiene; coaching to modify sleep habits; nightmare exposure; and rescripting of nightmares (Escamilla et al., 2012). The patient writes down the content of his or her nightmares and rewrites the nightmares to have triumphal endings. This rescripting technique is also effective in reducing nightmares. One possible mechanism for the effectiveness of this approach is in the reduction of posttraumatic cognitions.

A recent meta-analysis evaluated the effectiveness of psychological treatments for chronic nightmares (Hansen et al., 2013). Two psychological techniques were evaluated: imaginal confrontation with nightmare contents (ICNC) and imagery rescripting and rehearsal (IRR). Active suppression of distressing thoughts before sleeping increases the number of nightmares. ICNC tries to reduce the tendency to suppress thoughts related to nightmare contents and thereby reduce nightmares. In contrast, IRR involves rescripting nightmares and attaching a nondistressing ending to the target nightmare. Both techniques appeared to lower frequency of nightmares, nightmares per week, and subsequent PTSD severity.

The results of the meta-analysis indicated that higher duration of time for ICNC was associated with greater improvements, including reductions in nightmare frequency and in nights per week with nightmares (Hansen et al., 2013). This result implies that when ICNC is used and more time is spent on confronting nightmare content, long-term treatment responses are better. IRR, in contrast, can work in one session once patients know how to use this technique.

The effect sizes for psychological interventions for treating chronic nightmares are high, and these techniques have proven to be cost-effective. Yet patients are often unaware that chronic nightmares can be easily treated. These findings suggest that early intervention can prevent the nightmares from becoming chronic and thus improve quality of life.

Acceptability of Approaches

In a study, 27 veterans with either PTSD or traumatic brain injury (TBI) were asked to rate various sleep modalities in terms of their acceptability and preferences (Epstein, Babcock-Parziale, Haynes, & Herb, 2012). The providers found that relaxation therapy and pharmacotherapy were the treatments that these veterans most accepted and that they preferred. The veterans considered pharmacotherapy a quick fix that fit in with their schedules. However, there was some concern about dependency, and they wanted to stop. The veterans expressed desire for combined treatments: behavioral education with short-term or intermittent use of medications, with the goal of discontinuation. They preferred mindfulness strategies to behavior therapy. Nightmares were mentioned as an especially difficult sleep problem. A recurring theme among study participants was that an intervention needed to fit the veterans' busy schedules. An initial assessment of a treatment needs to take into account attendance, attrition, adherence, frequency and duration of intervention use. The challenge is to find a technique that will fit into the veterans' complex health problems and their difficult reintegration with family, friends, and work relationships.

In summary, sleep is a core characteristic of PTSD. Treating sleep problems reduces symptoms of PTSD. In contrast, treating trauma without treating sleep leads to incomplete results. Sleep-focused treatment for PTSD is both cost-effective and efficacious and should be integrated into all treatments for trauma (Spoormaker & Montgomery, 2008). This means screening for sleep issues and making appropriate referrals.

Summary and Clinical Considerations

At present, there are multiple evidence-based treatments for reducing acute and chronic PTSD and associated sleep disturbances. Several treatment guidelines are available to assist clinicians with the selection and implementation of appropriate treatments. Treatment guidelines typically recommend CBT interventions, such as prolonged exposure therapy, CPT, and EMDR. Additional treatment recommendations include stress inoculation treatment and pharmacotherapy. Pharmocotherapies, such as SSRIs and SNRIs, have the most empirical support and may be useful adjuncts to psychotherapeutic approaches. Thus, collaboration with a psychiatrist may be an essential component of the treatment plan. A body of research has also emerged about the effectiveness of CBT approaches for sleep and nightmare disturbances associated with PTSD.

For acute traumatic stress reactions, a *wait and see* approach is recommended as a natural recovery process is believed to be activated posttrauma and should be respected. During this early phase of recovery, ongoing monitoring and assessment is recommended to determine whether and when psychological support is needed. Psychological debriefing is *not* recommended as a front-line treatment for acute traumatic stress reactions.

In addition to level of empirical support available for various trauma-focused interventions, treatment selection can be made based on client characteristics (e.g., level of symptom severity, presence of co-occurring conditions, functional impairment, and level of social support), therapist level of training and expertise in implementing a particular treatment, and client's preference for a particular therapeutic approach (e.g., is the client willing to access and emotionally process the trauma and/or engage in homework assignments outside of the session?). To maximize the probability of success of the treatment, these factors should be assessed and discussed with the client prior to starting treatment.

Other clinical issues to consider when treating PTSD include gender and sociocultural (e.g., race or ethnicity, culture, socioeconomic status) factors in the experience, expression, and treatment of PTSD. Clinicians should be mindful of the ways in which trauma may manifest itself differently based on different identities and realize that clients' perceptions of and expectations for treatment may be influenced by these multicultural factors (Briere & Scott, 2012). Development of cultural competence in the provision of trauma treatment is thus vital (Brown, 2008). Overall, the establishment of a strong, positive therapeutic alliance is essential to providing a safe context in which clients can process their trauma experiences and regain a sense of psychological stability and empowerment (Briere & Scott, 2012).

REFERENCES

Beck, J. S. (2011). *Cognitive-behavior therapy: Basics and beyond* (2nd ed.). New York, NY: Guilford Press.

Belleville, G., Guay, S., & Marchand, A. (2009). Impact of sleep disturbances on PTSD symptoms and perceived health. *Journal of Nervous & Mental Disease, 197*(2), 126–132.

Bisson, J. I., McFarlane, A. I., Rose, S., Ruzek, J. I., & Watson, P. J. (2009). Psychological debriefing for adults. In E. B. Foa, T. M. Keane, M. J. Friedman, & J. Cohen (Eds.), *Effective treatments for PTSD: Practice guidelines from the International Society for Traumatic Stress Studies* (2nd ed., pp. 83–105). New York, NY: Guilford Press.

Briere, J., & Scott, C. (2012). *Principles of trauma therapy* (2nd ed.). New York, NY: Sage Publications.

Bronstein, I., & Montgomery, P. (2013). Sleeping patterns of Afghan unaccompanied asylum-seeking adolescents: A large observational study. *PLoS One, 8*. doi:10.1371/journal.pone.0056156

Brown, L. S. (2008). *Cultural competence in trauma therapy: Beyond the flashback*. Washington, DC: American Psychological Association.

Cahill, S. P., Rothbaum, B. O., Resick, P. A., & Follette, V. M. (2009). Cognitive–behavioral therapy for adults. In E. B. Foa, T. M. Keane,

M. J. Friedman, & J. Cohen (Eds.), *Effective treatments for PTSD: Practice guidelines from the International Society for Traumatic Stress Studies* (2nd ed., pp. 139–222). New York, NY: Guilford Press.

Chard, K. M., Ricksecker, E. G., Healy, E. T., Karlin, B. E., & Resick, P. A. (2012). Dissemination and experience with cognitive processing therapy. *Journal of Rehabilitation Research and Development, 49*(5), 667–678.

Clum, G. A., Nishith, P., & Resick, P. A. (2001). Trauma-related sleep disturbance and self-reported physical health symptoms in treatment-seeking female rape victims. *Journal of Nervous & Mental Disease, 189*, 618–622.

Epstein, D. R., Babcock-Parziale, J. L., Haynes, P. L., & Herb, C. A. (2012). Insomnia treatment acceptability and preferences of male Iraq and Afghanistan combat veterans and their healthcare providers. *Journal of Rehabilitation Research and Development, 49*(6), 867–878.

Escamilla, M., LaVoy, M., Moore, B. A., & Krakow, B. (2012). Management of posttraumatic nightmares: A review of pharmacologic and nonpharmacologic treatments since 2010. *Current Psychiatry Reports, 14*, 529–535.

Foa, E. B., Dancu, C. V., Hembree, E. A., Jaycox, L. H., Meadows, E. A., & Street, G. P. (1999). A comparison of exposure therapy, stress inoculation training, and their combination for reducing posttraumatic stress disorder in female assault victims. *Journal of Consulting and Clinical Psychology, 67*(2), 194. doi:10.1037/0022-006X.67.2.194

Foa, E. B., Hembree, E., & Rothbaum, B. O. (2007). *Prolonged exposure therapy for PTSD: Emotional processing of traumatic experiences: Therapist guide.* New York, NY: Oxford University Press.

Foa, E. B., Huppert, J. D., & Cahill, S. P. (2006). Emotional processing theory: An update. In B. O. Rothbaum (Ed.), *Pathological anxiety: Emotional processing in etiology and treatment* (pp. 3–24). New York, NY: Guilford Press.

Foa, E. B., Keane, T. M., Friedman, M. J., & Cohen, J. A. (2009). *Effective treatments for PTSD: Practice guidelines from the International Society for Traumatic Stress Studies* (2nd ed.). New York, NY: Guilford Press.

Foa, E. B., & Kozak, M. J. (1986). Emotional processing of fear: Exposure to corrective information. *Psychological Bulletin, 99*(1), 20–35. doi:10.1037/0033-2909.99.1.20

Foa, E. B., Rothbaum, B. O., Riggs, D. S., & Murdock, T. B. (1991). Treatment of posttraumatic stress disorder in rape victims: A comparison between cognitive–behavioral procedures and counseling. *Journal of Consulting and Clinical Psychology, 59*(5), 715.

Forbes, D., Creamer, M., Bisson, J. I., Cohen, J. A., Crow, B. E., Foa, E. B., et al. (2010). A guide to guidelines for the treatment of PTSD and related conditions. *Journal of Traumatic Stress, 23*(5), 537–552. doi:10.1002/jts.20565

Friedman, M. J., Davidson, J. R. T., & Stein, D. J. (2009). Psychopharmacotherapy for adults. In E. B. Foa, T. M. Keane, M. J. Friedman, & J. Cohen (Eds.), *Effective treatments for PTSD: Practice guidelines from the International Society for Traumatic Stress Studies* (2nd ed., pp. 245–268). New York, NY: Guilford Press.

Hansen, K., Hofling, V., Kroner-Borowik, T., Stangier, U., & Steil, R. (2013). Efficacy of psychological interventions aiming to reduce chronic nightmares: A meta-analysis. *Clinical Psychology Review, 33*, 146–155.

Jeffreys, M., Capehart, B., & Friedman, M. J. (2012). Pharmacotherapy for posttraumatic stress disorder: Review with clinical applications. *Journal of Rehabilitation Research and Development, 49*(5), 703–715.

Krakow, B., Krakow, J., Ulibarri, V. A., & Krakow, J. (2012). Nocturnal time monitoring behavior ("clock watching") in patients presenting to a sleep medical center with insomnia and posttraumatic stress symptoms. *Journal of Nervous and Mental Disease, 200*(9), 821–825.

Krakow, B., Ribeiro, J. D., Ulibarri, V. A., Krakow, J., & Joiner, T. E. (2011). Sleep disturbances and suicidal ideation in sleep medical center patients. *Journal of Affective Disorders, 131*, 422–427.

Lang, P. J. (1979). A bio-informational theory of emotional imagery. *Psychophysiology, 16*(6), 495–512. doi:10.1111/j.1469-8986.1979.tb01511.x

Management of Post-Traumatic Stress Working Group. (2010). *VA/DoD clinical practice guideline for management of post-traumatic stress.* Washington, DC: Department of Veterans Affairs, Department of Defense.

Meichenbaum, D. (1985). *Stress inoculation training.* Elmsford, NY: Pergamon Press.

Meichenbaum, D. (1996). Stress inoculation training for coping with stressors. *The Clinical Psychologist, 49*(1), 4–7.

Meichenbaum, D. (2008). Stress inoculation training: A preventative and treatment approach. In P. M. Lehrer, R. L. Woolfolk, & W. S. Sime (Eds.), *Principles and practice of stress management* (3rd ed., pp. 497–518). New York, NY: Guilford Press.

Morin, C. M. (2004). Cognitive–behavioral approaches to the treatment of insomnia. *Journal of Clinical Psychiatry, 65*(Suppl. 16), 33–40.

Morin, C. M., & Ware, J. C. (1996). Sleep and psychopathology. *Applied and Preventive Psychology, 5*, 211–224.

Nappi, C. M., Drummond, S. P. A., & Hall, J. M. H. (2012). Treating nightmares and insomnia in posttraumatic stress disorder: A review of current evidence. *Neuropharmacology, 62*, 576–585.

Olatunji, B. O., Deacon, B. J., & Abramowitz, J. S. (2009). The cruelest cure? Ethical issues in the implementation of exposure-based treatments. *Cognitive and Behavioral Practice, 16*(2), 172–180. doi:10.1016/j.cbpra.2008.07.003

Rachman, S. (1980). Emotional processing. *Behaviour Research and Therapy, 18*(1), 51–60. doi:10.1016/0005-7967(80)90069-8

Rauch, S., & Foa, E. (2006). Emotional processing theory (EPT) and exposure therapy for PTSD. *Journal of Contemporary Psychotherapy, 36*(2), 61–65. doi:10.1007/s10879-006-9008-y

Rauch, S. A., Eftekhari, A., & Ruzek, J. I. (2012). Review of exposure therapy: A gold standard for PTSD treatment. *Journal of Rehabilitation Research and Development, 49*, 679–687.

Resick, P. A., Galovski, T. E., Uhlmansiek, M. O. B., Scher, C. D., Clum, G. A., & Young-Xu, Y. (2008). A randomized clinical trial to dismantle components of cognitive processing therapy for posttraumatic stress disorder in female victims of interpersonal violence. *Journal of Consulting and Clinical Psychology, 76*(2), 243.

Resick, P. A., Monson, C. M., & Chard, K. M. (2007). *Cognitive processing therapy: Veteran/military version.* Washington, DC: Department of Veterans Affairs.

Resick, P. A., & Schnicke, M. K. (1993). *Cognitive processing therapy for rape victims: A treatment manual.* Newbury Park, CA: Sage.

Ribeiro, J. D., Pease, J. L., Gutierrez, P. M., Silva, C., Bernert, R. A., Rudd, M. D., & Joiner, T. E. (2012). Sleep problems outperform depression and hopelessness as cross-sectional and longitudinal predictors of suicidal ideation and behavior in young adults in the military. *Journal of Affective Disorders, 136*, 743–750.

Rosen, C., Adler, E., & Tiet, Q. (2013). Presenting concerns of veterans entering treatment for posttraumatic stress disorder. *Journal of Traumatic Stress, 26,* 640–643.

Schubert, S. J., Lee, C. W., & Drummond, P. D. (2011). The efficacy and psychophysiological correlates of dual-attention tasks in eye movement desensitization and reprocessing (EMDR). *Journal of Anxiety Disorders, 25*(1), 1–11. doi:10.1016/j.janxdis.2010.06.024

Shapiro, F. (2001). *Eye movement desensitization and reprocessing.* New York, NY: Guilford Press.

Shapiro, F., & Maxfield, L. (2002). Eye movement desensitization and reprocessing (EMDR): Information processing in the treatment of trauma. *Journal of Clinical Psychology, 58*(8), 933–946. doi:10.1002/jclp.10068

Spates, C. R., Koch, E., Cusack, K., Pagoto, S. L., & Waller, S. (2008). Eye movement desensitization and reprocessing. In E. B. Foa, T. M. Keane, M. J. Friedman, & J. Cohen (Eds.), *Effective treatments for PTSD: Practice guidelines from the International Society for Traumatic Stress Studies* (2nd ed., pp. 227–305). New York, NY: Guilford Press.

Spoormaker, V. I., & Montgomery, P. (2008). Disturbed sleep in posttraumatic stress disorder: Secondary symptom or core feature? *Sleep Medicine Reviews, 12,* 169–184.

Stein, D. J., Ipser, J. C., & Seedat, S. (2006). Pharmacotherapy for post traumatic stress disorder (PTSD). *Cochrane Database of Systematic Reviews, 1,* CD002795.

Stepanski, E. J., & Perlis, M. (2000). Behavioral sleep medicine: An emerging subspecialty in health psychology and sleep medicine. *Journal of Psychosomatic Research, 49,* 343–347.

Sullivan, G. M., & Neria, Y. (2009). Pharmacotherapy of PTSD: Current status and controversies. *Psychiatric Annals, 39*(6), 342.

Complementary and Alternative Medicine Treatments for Posttraumatic Stress Disorder

omplementary and alternative medicine (CAM) includes a range of therapies and health care systems, practices, and products that are outside of standard medical practice in the United States (Kim et al., 2013; Longacre, Silver-Highfield, Lama, & Grodin, 2012). In the United States, CAM treatments have become a $34 billion industry. These modalities are popular because patients find them effective and less invasive, more holistic than allopathic (or traditional Western) medicine. The boundaries between CAM and conventional medicine are often blurry.

Some CAM practices have become widely accepted, but others are still relatively obscure (Longacre et al., 2012). For patients born outside the United States, CAM modalities may represent primary health care, not something that is complementary. The popularity of these modalities is likely to continue to increase.

CAM treatments generally have fewer side effects and address the range of symptoms that patients with complex disorders, such as posttraumatic stress disorder (PTSD), experience. Even the U.S. Department of Veterans Affairs (VA), which typically represents a more mainstream approach, has acknowledged demand for CAM approaches among its patient population.

> The VA is committed to providing cutting-edge, evidence-based treatment for all Veterans, including those seeking PTSD-related services. Complementary and Alternative Medicine (CAM) interventions are widely requested and used by mental health consumers, including Veterans and active-duty personnel. CAM treatments are perceived to be less invasive and to have fewer side effects than traditional therapies and, in some cases, may be more congruent with individual treatment preference. VA is committed to expanding the evidence base and breadth of PTSD-related services available to Veterans. To this end, there is growing interest in applications of CAM. (Williams, Gierisch, McDuffie, Strauss, & Nagi, 2011, p. 3)

Consumer demand for these approaches is well documented. The key question is whether they work. A recent evidence-based synthesis issued by the VA reviewed the evidence by examining review articles describing CAM modalities for treatment of PTSD (Williams et al., 2011). The conclusion of this report was not promising, at least so far. Most of the evidence was for mind–body techniques, such as acupuncture and yoga. The report did find that meditation appeared to be a promising treatment, but noncompliance rates were high. Relaxation breathing appears promising. Acupuncture shows promise for treating depression. Finally, mindfulness-based stress reduction shows promise, but the studies were of fair-to-poor quality. They found no evidence to support body-based interventions, such as massage or spinal manipulation. They also found no evidence to support energy therapies, such as Reiki or healing touch (Williams et al., 2011).

In the 3 years since this report was written, there have been several new studies on the efficacy of many of these techniques. Although the data are still preliminary, they do show promise. Several of these techniques show promise as possible treatments for many of the most troublesome symptoms of PTSD and may become more mainstream over the next decade if evidence supports their use.

In contrast, a review of the literature on CAM approaches for refugees and torture survivors found support for several modalities but no literature to support others (Longacre et al., 2012). Modalities with support included meditation, dance and movement, spirituality, music, acupuncture and traditional Chinese medicine, Qigong/Tai Chi, and Reiki. Modalities with no articles available included Ayurveda, Pranayama/yogic breathing, massage, yoga, chiropractic therapy, homeopathy, and aromatherapy.

Although there was no literature that supported some of these approaches with refugees and torture survivors, the authors argue that most of these are potentially helpful adjuncts to more conventional treatments. In fact, CAM approaches may seem more in line with the patients' own understanding of their condition. In addition, CAM approaches may be more effective in addressing the complex sequelae of trauma, such as chronic pain, major depression, and somatization, which are not easily addressed via allopathic medicine. CAM modalities can be offered in the community and can reinforce effective continuity of care for people who have experienced trauma.

Following is a summary of several CAM modalities that have been used to treat trauma survivors and that have some empirical support. Given the interest in these modalities, we expect that more studies will be conducted, thus furthering the evidence base.

ACUPUNCTURE

Acupuncture is one of the most mainstream of the CAM treatments. It is based on traditional Chinese medicine (TCM) and involves inserting very thin needles along meridian points to stimulate the flow of energy or *chi* (Kim et al., 2013). Electroacupuncture is another form of acupuncture wherein needles are inserted along meridian points and electric current is passed between pairs of acupuncture needles.

In a randomized trial of 138 patients following the Wenchun earthquake in China, researchers compared the effectiveness of electroacupuncture to paroxetine (Paxil; Wang, Hu, Wang, Pang, & Zhang, 2012). The electroacupuncture group was treated with four acupuncture points on the scalp. The patients were treated for 30 minutes every other day for up to 12 weeks. Patients in the Paxil group were also treated for 12 weeks. Patients' levels of PTSD, depression, and anxiety were assessed at 6 weeks, 12 weeks, 3 months, and 6 months. At each assessment point, the patients treated with electroacupuncture had lower levels of PTSD, depression, and anxiety than those treated with paroxetine.

Kim and colleagues (2013) conducted a recent systematic review of trials testing the efficacy of acupuncture in treating PTSD. They included article databases in English, Korean, Japanese, and Chinese. They found that four randomized trials and two unrandomized trials met their inclusion criteria out of 136 articles first identified.

The four randomized trials included 543 PTSD patients, with a mean sample size of 49 per treatment arm. The duration of treatment in the trials ranged from 1 to 12 weeks. One study compared needle acupuncture with cognitive behavioral therapy (CBT) and a waitlist condition. Another compared electroacupuncture with moxibustion or auricular (ear) acupuncture with SSRIs. Another randomized controlled trial (RCT) compared electroacupuncture plus moxibustion with oral SSRIs. The final

RCT included in their analysis was acupoint stimulation plus CBT versus CBT alone (Kim et al., 2013).

In the study comparing CBT/acupuncture versus waitlist control/CBT versus waitlist control, the researchers found no significant difference between acupuncture and CBT. Acupuncture was significantly more effective than waitlist on posttraumatic stress symptoms, depression, and impairment. CBT was significantly superior to waitlist on posttraumatic stress, depression, anxiety, and impairment (Kim et al., 2013).

Electroacupuncture was as effective as SSRIs in one RCT. And the addition of acupoint stimulation to CBT resulted in lower symptoms on the Impact of Events Scale in another. In two RCTs comparing electroacupuncture plus moxibustion to SSRIs, one study found no significant difference between the two. The other study found electroacupuncture plus moxibustion was actually superior to SSRIs on PTSD symptoms, depression, and anxiety (Kim et al., 2013).

Although the authors found the results of these studies promising, Kim et al. (2013) concluded that they were not cogent. Due to the small number of studies, they felt that it was premature to verify the efficacy of acupuncture, and recommended future studies, particularly those that include sham/placebo acupuncture as a control for the placebo effect in these studies.

A recent "review of reviews" found that while acupuncture did not alleviate PTSD symptoms directly, it lessened ancillary and comorbid symptoms that were part of the trauma spectrum response (Lee et al., 2012). A comprehensive search of meta-analyses and review articles yielded 1,480 citations, and 52 systematic reviews/meta-analyses. All but one of the 52 met the inclusion criteria. There were no reviews on PTSD or sexual function. The conclusion was that acupuncture does appear to be useful in treating symptoms that accompany PTSD and appears to be effective for treating headaches. It also appears promising for treating anxiety, sleep disturbances, depression, and chronic pain, but findings were mixed for many of these. There was no evidence to support use of acupuncture for substance abuse.

MINDFULNESS

Mindfulness is another CAM modality that has been integrated into trauma treatment. It is an approach that originated with Buddhism but that has been applied in a secular form. Simply put, mindfulness is a way of thinking and focusing that can help clients become more aware of their present experiences. It means paying attention to everyday experiences that you might let pass unnoticed: the taste of coffee, the feel of walking down the stairs, the sound of rain on the roof. Mindfulness involves paying attention to these experiences and the feelings and sensations associated with them.

Practicing mindfulness has two key components:

- Being *aware* in the present moment
- *Accepting* your thoughts and feelings without judging them

Being mindful means allowing thoughts and feelings to pass without either clinging to them or pushing them away. They just take their natural course. When you are distracted by thoughts about things other than your current experience, you just notice them and then redirect your attention back to the present (National Center for PTSD, 2010b).

Mindfulness Reduces Trauma Reactions

In a recent review, Dutton and colleagues (2013) described how mindfulness can help reduce symptoms of PTSD and depression and has been used with populations such as those who survived the war in Kosovo or who were child abuse survivors. According to the National Center for PTSD (2010a), mindfulness can help trauma survivors cope with difficult emotions, such as anxiety and depression. It will help them become more focused and aware of the present moment while also being more willing to experience some of the emotions that occur as a result of trauma. It can help trauma survivors pay more attention to their thoughts and feelings and just let them go rather than labeling them as "good" or "bad" or reacting to them with either avoidance or impulsive behavior.

Mindfulness can help trauma survivors develop more compassion toward themselves and others and become less critical of themselves. This is an important first step in recovery. The hypothesized mechanism is similar to other treatments for trauma, such as prolonged exposure therapy and EMDR. Mindfulness is thought to result in symptom reduction and behavior change, cognitive change, self-management, relaxation, and acceptance (Dutton et al., 2013).

Mindfulness can also help prepare trauma survivors for therapy by giving them the skills to handle their feelings. Mindfulness teaches survivors to know what is happening in their own bodies and minds and to cope with thoughts and feelings in a healthy way. It also helps reduce rumination, which is hypothesized to mediate the relationship between beliefs about the trauma memory and PTSD symptoms (Kearney, McDermott, Malte, Martinez, & Simpson, 2013). This knowledge can help trauma survivors persist in treatment even when it is difficult. Mindfulness could be used by itself or together with standard treatments (National Center for PTSD, 2010b).

One recent study randomized combat veterans with PTSD to receive mindfulness-based stress reduction (MBSR; $n = 25$) or usual care ($n = 22$; Kearney et al., 2013). MBSR is an 8-week class that teaches mindfulness. The sessions included formal mindfulness, which included body scan, Hatha yoga, seated and walking meditation; mindfulness techniques applied to everyday experiences; mindful inquiry, such as curiosity about the present moment; and nonjudgmental acceptance of one's own experience The participants in the study were assessed for PTSD, depression, and health-related quality of life posttreatment and in a 4-month follow-up. At the 4-month follow-up, more veterans in the mindfulness group had clinically significant changes in health-related quality of life and PTSD symptoms. When analyzing data on class completion (four or more classes attended), there were medium-to-large between-group effect sizes for depression, mental health–related quality of life, and mindfulness skills.

A qualitative study of MSBR with 10 low-income, minority women with a history of partner violence found three themes using an interpretive phenomenological methodology: struggles to practice meditation, a vision of growing and helping, and personal and interpersonal improvements (Bermudez et al., 2013). The participants reported that they were able to let the trauma associated with their partner violence, and other traumas, go after participating in the MSBR. They were also able to begin addressing both personal and professional goals (such as finishing school) and felt as if they had the tools to reduce their stress.

Participants in the study by Bermudez et al. (2013) reported that mindfulness helped them learn to quiet their minds, something that was novel for many of them. They also reported seeing themselves with more compassion, and that improved their self-concept. They described themselves as being more outgoing and as having improved relationships with their partners and friends. They learned to be more assertive in their relationships and express their needs without escalating. Once their own needs started being met, they found themselves realizing that others had needs, too, and learned to listen to those needs with patience and openness. Their relationships improved. As they became aware of the ways that partner violence had affected them, they learned to forgive themselves and, in some cases, their abusers. The authors felt that acceptance of self and emotional regulation may be seen as precursors to overcoming trauma.

Mindfulness can also be combined with cognitive therapy in an intervention called mindfulness-based cognitive therapy (MBCT; King et al., 2013). It, too, shows promise as a treatment for PTSD. In a pilot study of veterans with PTSD, four groups (*n* = 20) were assigned to MBCT and treatment as usual (three groups, *n* = 17 each). Patients who completed the program had a significant improvement in PTSD symptom severity on two measures. The symptoms most likely to improve were avoidance/numbing symptoms and PTSD-relevant cognitions, such as self-blame. The authors concluded that MBCT was an acceptable brief intervention/adjunctive therapy for combat-related PTSD and that it reduced avoidance symptoms and trauma-related cognitions. They recommended further trials with larger samples to verify its efficacy.

EXPRESSIVE WRITING

Another CAM treatment for trauma is expressive writing. Expressive writing is based on the work of James Pennebaker (Smyth, Hockemeyer, Heron, Wonderlich, & Pennebaker, 2008), who found that writing about major stress life events for a brief period over several days, even as few as 20 minutes per day, significantly reduced depression, anxiety, PTSD symptoms, and health problems. One mechanism by which expressive writing was thought to be effective was in helping trauma survivors come to grip with their experiences in the broader story of life and derive some meaning from their experiences (Koopman et al., 2005).

Forty-seven women who had experienced partner violence were randomly assigned to either an expressive-writing group or a neutral-writing condition (Koopman et al., 2005). The women had experienced severe levels of partner violence and had left their relationships an average of 5 years earlier. The expressive-writing group wrote about their most stressful or traumatic life experience. The neutral-writing group wrote about their daily schedules. There were a total of four writing sessions, and they were 20 minutes in length. The main effects for changes in PTSD, depression, or pain were not significant. However, among depressed women, expressive writing was related to a significant drop in depression. The authors concluded that for depressed women with a history of partner violence, expressive writing may help reduce symptoms of depression.

Another study also assigned participants with PTSD to either expressive-writing or neutral-writing conditions (Smyth, Hockemeyer, & Tulloch, 2008). Participants were recruited from either VA treatment programs or rape crisis centers. There were 25 who met the criteria for PTSD, and their traumatic experiences had occurred 6 months prior to the study. Follow-up assessments were conducted 3 months postwriting. Immediately after the writing intervention, those in the expressive-writing group showed more symptomatology than those in the neutral-writing condition. There were no significant changes in PTSD symptomatology based on writing condition. However, the expressive-writing group showed greater reductions in tension and anger. In addition, when exposed to trauma imagery, the experimental group showed an attenuation of the cortisol response compared to those in the control group. These data support the hypothesis that expressive writing attenuates the relationship between trauma-related thoughts and physical or psychological symptoms.

ANIMAL-ASSISTED THERAPY

There have been numerous recent news reports about programs that provide dogs for people with PTSD. According to the National Center for PTSD, owning a dog can help lift the mood of trauma survivors or lower their stress level (National Center for PTSD, 2012). Dogs can provide emotional support for people with PTSD and help them manage symptoms. Particularly relevant are emotional-support dogs. Emotional-support dogs help owners feel better by giving friendship and love.

An emotional-support dog does not need special training. Generally, a regular pet can be an emotional-support dog if a mental health provider writes a letter saying that the owner has a mental health condition or disability and needs the dog's help for his or her health or treatment.

In most states, emotional-support dogs do not have special permission to go to all public places as service dogs do, but sometimes they can. For example, the owner may be able to get permission to have an emotional-support dog in a house or apartment that does not normally allow dogs, or to fly on a plane together with the dog. The rationale for the inclusion of therapy dogs is that they create a safe environment of trust and acceptance (Dietz, Davis, & Pennings, 2013).

Dogs are not a substitute for treatment for PTSD but can be an important adjunct. Research on the effectiveness of animal-assisted therapy for PTSD is still in its early stages. One recent study found that animal-assisted therapy was effective in relieving trauma symptoms for children aged 7 to 17 who had been sexually abused (Dietz et al., 2013). In this study, the children were assigned to one of three groups that compared animal-assisted therapy with therapeutic stories. Two of the groups included therapy dogs: The groups were stories only, stories with dog, and dog only. Children assigned to the groups with the dogs had significant decreases in anxiety, depression, anger, PTSD, dissociation, and sexual concerns. Stories with dogs was the most effective treatment overall. Further research will be needed to verify the efficacy of this approach.

CONCLUSION

CAM approaches are popular and show promise as important treatments for PTSD. They can be used alone or as adjuncts to traditional treatments and can help manage the complex symptoms of PTSD and co-occurring conditions, such as chronic pain and depression. The preliminary data are encouraging, but further studies will be needed to establish the efficacy of these approaches.

REFERENCES

Bermudez, D., Benjamin, M. T., Porter, S. E., Saunders, P. A., Myers, N. A. L., & Dutton, M. A. (2013). A qualitative analysis of beginning mindfulness experiences for women with posttraumatic stress disorder and a history of intimate partner violence. *Complementary Therapies in Clinical Practice, 19*, 104–108.

Dietz, T. J., Davis, D., & Pennings, J. (2013). Evaluating animal-assisted therapy in group treatment for child sexual abuse. *Journal of Child Sexual Abuse, 21*(6), 665–683.

Dutton, M. A., Bermudez, D., Matas, A., Majid, H., & Myers, N. L. (2013). Mindfulness-based stress reduction for low-income, predominantly African American women with PTSD and a history of intimate partner violence. *Cognitive & Behavioral Practice, 20*, 23–32.

Kearney, D. J., McDermott, K., Malte, C., Martinez, M., & Simpson, T. L. (2013). Effects of participation in a mindfulness program for veterans with posttraumatic stress disorder: A randomized controlled pilot study. *Journal of Clinical Psychology, 69*, 14–27.

Kim, Y.-D., Heo, I., Shin, B.-C., Crawford, C., Kang, H.-W., & Lim, J.-H. (2013). Acupuncture for posttraumatic stress disorder: A systematic review of randomized controlled trials and prospective clinical trials. *Evidence-Based Complementary and Alternative Medicine, 2013*, Article ID 615857. Retrieved from http://dx.doi.org/10.1155/2013/615857

King, A. P., Erickson, T. M., Giardino, N. D., Favorite, T., Rauch, S. A. M., Robinson, E., . . . Liberzon, I. (2013). A pilot study of group mindfulness-based cognitive therapy (MBCT) for combat veterans with posttraumatic stress disorder (PTSD). *Depression & Anxiety, 30*, 638–645.

Koopman, C., Ismailji, T., Holmes, D., Classen, C. C., Palesh, O., & Wales, T. (2005). The effects of expressive writing on pain, depression and posttraumatic stress disorder symptoms in survivors of intimate partner violence. *Journal of Health Psychology, 10*(2), 211–221.

Lee, C., Crawford, C., Wallerstedt, D., York, A., Duncan, A., Smith, J., . . . Jonas, W. (2012). The effectiveness of acupuncture research across components of the trauma spectrum response (tsr):

A systematic review of reviews. *Systematic Reviews, 1*, 49. Retrieved from http://www.systematicreviewsjournal.com/content/1/1/46

Longacre, M., Silver-Highfield, E., Lama, P., & Grodin, M. A. (2012). Complementary and alternative medicine in the treatment of refugees and survivors of torture: A review and proposal for action. *Torture, 22*(1), 38–57.

National Center for PTSD. (2010a). *Effects of PTSD on family.* Retrieved from http://www.ptsd.va.gov/public/pages/effects-ptsd-family.asp

National Center for PTSD. (2010b). *Mindfulness practice in the treatment of traumatic stress.* Retrieved from http://www.ptsd.va.gov/public/pages/mindful-ptsd.asp

National Center for PTSD. (2012). *Dogs and PTSD.* Retrieved from http://www.ptsd.va.gov/public/pages/dogs_and_ptsd.asp

Smyth, J. M., Hockemeyer, J. R., Heron, K. E., Wonderlich, S. A., & Pennebaker, J. W. (2008). Prevalence, type, disclosure, and severity of adverse life events in college students. *Journal of American College Health, 57*(1), 69–76.

Smyth, J. M., Hockemeyer, J. R., & Tulloch, H. (2008). Expressive writing and post-traumatic stress disorder: Effects on trauma symptoms, mood states, and cortisol reactivity. *British Journal of Health Psychology, 13*, 85–93.

Wang, Y., Hu, Y.-P., Wang, W.-C., Pang, R.-Z., & Zhang, A.-R. (2012). Clinical studies on treatment of earthquake-caused posttraumatic stress disorder using electroacupuncture. *Evidence-Based Complementary and Alternative Medicine.* doi:10.1155/2012/431279

Williams, J. W., Gierisch, J. M., McDuffie, J., Strauss, J. L., & Nagi, A. (2011). *An overview of complementary and alternative medicine therapies for anxiety and depressive disorders: Supplement to efficacy of complementary and alternative medicine therapies for posttraumatic stress disorder.* Washington, DC: Health Service Research & Development Service.

Questions and Controversies in Trauma Psychology

he scientific study of psychological trauma is relatively young compared to other fields in psychology, with the official addition of posttraumatic stress disorder (PTSD) only occurring in 1980 with the release of the third edition of the *Diagnostic and Statistical Manual of Mental Disorders* (*DSM-III*; American Psychiatric Association [APA], 1980). Since then, psychologists have systematically attempted to understand the risk and protective factors associated with trauma exposure, as well as the best way to assess and treat PTSD. There are certain key agreements that bind the field of trauma psychology together. However, several important and long-standing questions remain.

In this chapter, we discuss three key controversies in the trauma psychology field: (1) whether PTSD is a sufficient diagnostic category to capture the full range of reactions to severe and prolonged trauma (or whether another diagnostic category is needed, such as complex PTSD [CPTSD] or disorders of extreme stress not otherwise specified [DESNOS]), (2) whether memories of traumatic events can be lost and then later remembered, and (3) whether dissociative identity disorder (formerly known as multiple personality disorder) is a real condition or a social construct.

COMPLEX POSTTRAUMATIC STRESS DISORDER: DISTINCT FROM PTSD?

Complex trauma is defined as exposure to severe, repeated, and prolonged interpersonal traumatic events, such as physical and sexual abuse, chronic domestic violence, or torture. Exposure to complex trauma typically spans many years and involves situations wherein the individual had little to no control over the experience or escape was impossible (Courtois, 2004; Herman, 1992). A subgroup of researchers in the trauma field argue that the psychopathological responses to complex trauma may not be adequately captured by the diagnostic category of PTSD, and they recommend alternative categories such as CPTSD (Cloitre et al., 2011; Courtois, 2004; Herman, 1992; van der Kolk, 2002) or DESNOS (Pelcovitz et al., 1997; van der Kolk, Roth, Pelcovitz, Sunday, & Spinazzola, 2005).

These theorists posit that the disturbances in response to complex trauma are typically widespread and entail chronic difficulties in self-regulatory capacities that go above and beyond the symptom clusters of PTSD. These difficulties cut across six domains: (1) emotion regulation problems, (2) disturbances in relational capacities, (3) alterations in attention and concentration (e.g., amnesia or dissociation), (4) alterations in self-perception, (5) somatic distress or disorganization, and (6) alterations in belief systems (Cloitre et al., 2011; Resick et al., 2012).

The diagnostic category of DESNOS was tested during the field trials for the *DSM-IV* (APA, 1997). Findings revealed that

92% of individuals diagnosed with DESNOS were also diagnosed with PTSD (van der Kolk et al., 2005). Given the significant overlap between the two constructs, DESNOS was not included as a separate category in the *DSM-IV*. The symptoms of DESNOS, however, were included as associated features of PTSD in the *DSM-IV-TR* (APA, 2000). Nevertheless, the identification and description of the core symptom domains in DESNOS or CPTSD brought significant attention to the differences in adaptations that can occur after exposure to severe and prolonged trauma and also allowed for the development and testing of assessment measures and treatment approaches to treat these disturbances (Cloitre et al., 2011; Resick et al., 2012). Since the *DSM-IV* field trials, several studies have attempted to validate the categories of CPTSD/DESNOS in order to support its inclusion in the *DSM* (Courtois, 2004; Ford, 1999; Scoboria, Ford, Lin, & Frisman, 2008).

Critics of CTPSD, however, question whether these constructs amount to a valid or reliable diagnosis and whether they incrementally add to the assessment and treatment of individuals with posttraumatic disturbances (Keane & Najavits, 2013; Resick et al., 2012). Resick et al. (2012) conducted a comprehensive review of the research on CTPSD to determine whether the construct of CPTSD can be measured reliably, whether it is distinct from other disorders, and whether it has clinical utility in terms of the type or duration of treatment used for this condition. Several of their findings are highlighted below.

Measurement of Symptoms of DESNOS or CPTSD

To date, only one measure of DESNOS has been developed; none is available for CPTSD (Resick et al., 2012). The Structured Interview for Disorders of Extreme Stress (SIDES; Scoboria et al., 2008) is a 45-item clinical interview designed to assess the six symptom clusters of DESNOS. A self-report version of the SIDES also exists. Resick et al. argued that the SIDES has several problems that limit its utility: (1) The measure does not link the symptoms assessed to a specific trauma exposure; thus it is unclear whether trauma is an etiological factor in DESNOS symptoms; also (2) there is a lack of consistency across studies in scoring the SIDES, which results in difficulties interpreting research findings.

Since there are no measures designed to assess CPTSD, multiple measures are often administered that tap into distinct self-regulatory disturbances (one measure to assess dissociation, another to assess relationship disturbances, yet another to assess somatization, and so forth). Resick et al. point to the limitations inherent in utilizing multiple measures to detect CPTSD, including that the individual measures were not originally designed to assess the construct of CPTSD, that the individual measures do not link the symptoms to a specific trauma, and that use of multiple measures prevents the establishment of diagnostic rules and cutoff scores to aid in diagnostic assessment. Overall, there is a call for more specific measures to aid in the establishment of the construct validity of CPTSD (Resick et al., 2012).

Overlap Between CPTSD, PTSD, and Borderline Personality Disorder

Another key criticism of CPTSD is its significant overlap with PTSD and Borderline Personality Disorder (BPD; Lewis & Grenyer, 2009; Resick et al., 2012). Bryant (2012) argued, however, that the overlap between CPTSD and PTSD is acceptable because CPTSD is in fact a variant of PTSD. Supporters also argue that the conditions of CPTSD or DESNOS are different in terms of symptom profile and level of impairment when compared to PTSD (e.g., Courtois, 2004; Luxenberg, Spinazzola, & van der Kolk, 2001). Moreover, Ford (1999) found that despite the significant comorbidity between DESNOS and PTSD, a small subgroup of traumatized individuals were diagnosed with DESNOS without co-occurring PTSD, suggesting DESNOS was distinct and could occur independently of PTSD.

Relatedly, the overlap between CPTSD and BPD has been widely noted and heavily debated (Lewis & Grenyer, 2009). BPD is characterized by difficulties with emotion regulation, impulsive and self-destructive behaviors, self-perception problems, and interpersonal difficulties (Lewis & Grenyer, 2009), all of which are similar to the symptom domains of CPTSD. Some argue that BPD should be reconceptualized as CPTSD. This recommendation is based on the assumption that trauma is also an etiological factor in the development of BPD. However, studies show that a significant subgroup of individuals diagnosed with BPD do not have a trauma history and that 42% of the variance in BPD symptoms is accounted for by genetic factors (Lewis & Grenyer, 2009), suggesting that the disorders are distinct despite the conceptual overlap. In fact, Luxenberg et al. (2001) argue that the primary symptom of CPTSD/DESNOS is affect dysregulation, whereas for BPD, the hallmark symptoms are relationship and identity disturbances. Thus, BPD is best conceptualized as a disorder of attachment, whereas CPTSD is a disorder of self-regulation (Luxenberg et al., 2001). Nevertheless, the overlap between CPTSD and other psychiatric conditions reduces its distinctiveness as a separate diagnosis.

Do Standard PTSD Treatments Work for Individuals With CPTSD?

Although several textbooks have been written on the assessment and treatment of CPTSD (Courtois & Ford, 2009, 2012), there have been few clinical trials testing the efficacy of treatments for this population. Thus it is unclear whether standard PTSD treatments are efficacious for this population. Those who argue for the distinctness of CPTSD point to the need for treatments that go beyond the processing of trauma memories, beliefs, and emotions (van der Kolk et al., 2005). Rather, they say, treatment should first address key disturbances, such as emotion regulation problems, dissociation, and interpersonal difficulties, instead of the standard symptoms clusters of PTSD.

Cloitre et al. (2011) reviewed several studies that showed that compared to individuals without CPTSD, individuals with CPTSD may not respond as optimally to standard PTSD treatments, suggesting that these treatments may need to be modified to optimize treatment outcomes for those with CPTSD. A survey of 50 experts (25 complex PTSD experts and 25 classic PTSD experts) revealed significant agreement on the characteristics of CPTSD and consensus on the most appropriate treatment for this condition (Cloitre et al., 2011), with the majority endorsing a sequential or phase-based treatment approach that targets specific symptom sets.

Summary

Despite the clinical utility of CPTSD, there is insufficient evidence to support the validity and reliability of the construct, so it was not included in the most recent edition of the *DSM* (*DSM-5*, APA, 2013). Because the symptom profile of CPTSD overlaps significantly with that of PTSD and other conditions, the general consensus has been that it is more parsimonious to assign one diagnosis (PTSD) than two. Nevertheless, the recent changes in the diagnostic category of PTSD now allow for a dissociative subtype of PTSD, which taps into one of the key domains of CPTSD (Lanius et al., 2010). CPTSD has been widely hailed as a clinical construct since it brought much-needed attention to the ways in which individuals may respond to severe and prolonged traumas compared to single-incident traumas and highlights the ways in which developmental theory can shed light on the effects of complex trauma that occurs during childhood or adolescence.

TRAUMA AND THE "MEMORY WARS"

Another controversial and heavily debated topic in the field of trauma psychology is whether memories of childhood abuse can be lost and then later recovered (Dalenberg, 2006;

Goodman, Quas, & Ogle, 2010; Lindsay & Briere, 1997; Lindsay & Read, 2001). Historically, the clinical, scientific, and legal communities have been split between two camps: those who believe that traumatic amnesia (i.e., memory loss of traumatic events) does exist and that lost memories can be later recalled (Dalenberg, 2006; Lindsay & Briere, 1997), and those who argue that traumatic memories are rarely lost for years and then later recovered and that in fact some "recovered" memories may not be real, but rather false memories (Loftus & Ketcham, 1994; Ofshe & Watters, 1994). Proponents of the latter view often blame overzealous clinicians who presumably used highly suggestive techniques (e.g., hypnosis, guided imagery) to elicit "false" memories from suggestible clients engaged in the process of trauma "memory work."

Research and debate on this issue have converged on several key questions: (1) Do recovered memories of traumatic events exist, and if so, how accurate are they? (2) How and why do individuals *forget* and then later remember a traumatic event? (3) Do false memories exist? (4) How and why do false memories occur? What follows is a brief review of the empirical and theoretical literature attempting to answer each of these questions. Points of convergence between the two schools of thought are discussed in the summary.

Do Recovered Memories of Trauma Exist, and If So, Are They Accurate?

Scientific evidence from multiple empirical studies, utilizing both retrospective and prospective designs with clinical and community samples, supports the notion that partial or complete amnesia for childhood traumatic or abuse experiences, and the subsequent recovery of these memories does occur among a small subgroup of traumatized individuals (Dalenberg, 2006; Goodman et al., 2003, 2010; Williams, 1994, 1995). Prospective studies (those that follow survivors of childhood abuse many years after a documented trauma) offer the strongest support and indicate that individuals can experience a traumatic event in childhood, forget it for a period of time, and then later recall it (Williams, 1994 & 1995; Widom & Morris, 1997).

For example, Williams (1994) interviewed 129 women 17 years after a documented childhood sexual abuse experience and asked them directly about their memories of the event. Thirty-eight percent of the women reported that they did not recall the sexual abuse they had experienced 17 years earlier, suggesting that they did not remember the documented trauma. Williams ruled out the possibility that the women were simply too embarrassed to report the index trauma by noting that they did report other episodes of sexual victimization. In Williams's view, this supports the idea that they simply did not remember or could not access the trauma memory in question.

Williams (1995) also found that of the 80 women who remembered the documented trauma, 16% reported that they had periods of time when they forgot the traumatic event and then later recalled the memory. Forgetting was associated with age at the time of the trauma (women who were very young at the time of the index trauma were more likely to have periods of forgetting) and whether they received support from their mother (women who received less support from their mother were less likely to remember the index trauma).

Another prospective study conducted by Widom and Morris (1997) examined adults with a documented history of abuse (sexual or physical) from 20 years earlier and found that 39% of the participants failed to report their trauma history, suggesting amnesia or an inability to recall their childhood trauma. Likewise, Goodman et al. (2003) questioned 174 older adolescents and young adults several times about their earlier documented history of childhood sexual abuse and involvement in criminal prosecution cases and found that 8% did not disclose or recall their documented history, again suggesting that they could not remember the experience.

Of importance to these findings is the question of whether recovered traumatic memories are accurate or reliable. Williams

(1995) found that individuals with recovered memories and individuals with continuous memories (memories that were never forgotten) of the index trauma were similar in their accuracy and consistency when comparing recounts of the index trauma to medical records of the index trauma from 17 years earlier.

Dalenberg (1996) conducted a follow-up study of 17 patients who reported recovered memories of trauma while in therapy with her and initiated a process whereby they collaboratively searched for evidence to corroborate or refute the memories. Corroborating information was gathered from the patients, the alleged perpetrators, and family members. Dalenberg found that there were no significant differences in the level of accuracy for client memories that were continuously remembered versus client memories that were recovered later in time, supporting the reliability of recovered memories. Studies suggest several factors are associated with traumatic amnesia: young age at the time of the abuse, severity and chronicity of abuse experiences, and lack of support around the time of the abuse (DePrince et al., 2012; Goodman et al., 2003; Williams, 1994).

In sum, these findings suggest that a small subgroup of individuals may experience amnesia or inability to recall past childhood traumatic experiences and that these lost memories can be later recovered as accurately as memories that were continuous. Moreover, survey studies indicate that the concepts of traumatic amnesia and recovered memories are well accepted in the scientific community (Dalenberg, 2006; Dammeyer, Nightingale, & McCoy, 1997), further bolstering the validity of these constructs.

How And Why Do Individuals Forget And Then Later Remember Traumatic Events?

While a definitive answer about the precise mechanism responsible for traumatic amnesia has yet to be determined, several psychological processes have been implicated in the forgetting of traumatic memories. Sigmund Freud (1915/1957) considered *repression*, an important psychological defense mechanism, responsible for pushing distressing traumatic memories outside of conscious awareness. After repressed traumatic memories were outside of conscious awareness, however, they were still presumed to indirectly influence the individual's thoughts, emotions, and behaviors. For example, a person who repressed a traumatic memory may nonetheless exhibit symptoms consistent with a history of trauma (e.g., difficulty managing emotional experiences or forming relationships). Repression is considered an involuntary and unconscious defense mechanism, often known as *motivated forgetting*, because it concerns traumatic or emotionally charged events. There is significant debate about whether repression is a useful concept in the explanation of traumatic amnesia, as it is difficult to formulate empirical measures with which to study its validity (Colangelo, 2009; Skinner, 2001).

In contrast, *dissociation* is a concept used in the explanation of traumatic amnesia that has had a wider acceptance in the trauma field (Janet, 1889; van der Kolk, 2002). Dissociation refers to a process whereby the mind splits apart or separates experiences, thoughts, feelings, and memories into different "streams of consciousness" (Colangelo, 2009; van der Kolk & van der Hart, 1991). Whereas repression is seen as a horizontal process that pushes traumatic memories deep below the surface and into the unconscious, dissociation is seen as a vertical process that splits memory off into an "alternate stream of consciousness" (Colangelo, 2009; van der Kolk & van der Hart, 1991).

The dissociated memories (though not remembered) are presumed to be closer to awareness than repressed memories and continue to influence the individual's present-day experience because, as van der Kolk (1994) famously stated, "the body keeps the score," and thus traumatic memories are expressed somatically. Decades of research studies have shown a consistent and moderate connection between a history of trauma and a tendency toward dissociation (Allen et al., 2002; Dalenberg et al., 2012), firmly cementing dissociation as a putative mechanism of traumatic amnesia.

Some researchers also argue that traumatic memories may be encoded and stored differently than nontraumatic memories (Straker, Watson, & Robinson, 2002). Studies have shown that exposure to severe and chronic traumatic events causes an increase in the secretion of stress hormones and changes in specific brain structures (i.e., the amygdala and hippocampus) that disrupt normal memory processes, resulting in traumatic memories being consolidated and stored differently than nontraumatic memories (Layton & Krikorian, 2002; van der Kolk, 1994).

Opponents of theories that involve traumatic repression and dissociation, however, argue it is not necessary to invoke special mechanisms to explain lost traumatic memories. Instead, they highlight alternative processes, such as *normal forgetting* and *childhood amnesia* (Kihlstrom, McNally, Loftus, & Pope, 2005; Loftus & Davis, 2006; Shobe & Kihlstrom, 1997). Based on eye-witness, experimental, and clinical neuroscience research, opponents argue that memories for traumatic or emotionally charged experiences tend to be vivid, persistent, and well remembered (Kihlstrom et al., 2005; Shobe & Kihlstrom, 1997). Moreover, memories for traumatic events are presumed to be similar to memories for nontraumatic events and thus are vulnerable to the same processes of ordinary forgetting over time.

One major reason for forgetting may be the failure to properly encode details of the experience into memory. Failure to encode may be due to stresses put upon one's attention during a traumatic event (Loftus et al., 1998). Thus, when one later attempts to retrieve the memory, it is difficult to access because there are missing retrieval cues, particular details that were not encoded appropriately. Critics of this perspective point to the lack of ecological validity of experimental studies conducted in a lab when compared to the direct experiences of abuse (Brewin, 2007).

Infantile/childhood amnesia is another possibility that refers to the unavailability of memories of events that occur before age 3 or 4. Researchers argue that both positive and negative memories are prone to childhood amnesia (including memories of sexual abuse), which would explain the forgetting of these memories (Loftus et al., 1998; Shobe & Kihlstrom, 1997).

Forgetting, it is argued, can also be explained by the failure of a young child to understand the nature of the abusive situation at the time, or the event may not have been perceived as traumatic at the time—thus "forgetting" should not be perceived as repression or dissociation but rather as failure to interpret the event as abusive or traumatic (Loftus & Davis, 2006; McNally & Geraerts, 2009).

Two prominent trauma theories have attempted to provide a possible reconciliation between the perspectives of repression/dissociation and infantile amnesia/normal forgetting. First, Lenore Terr (1994), in her work with traumatized children, made a distinction between Type I and Type II traumas. Type I traumas are time-limited "single-blow" events (e.g., car crash or sudden unexpected death of a loved one) that characteristically lead to memories that are detailed and clear. In contrast, Type II traumas, repeated and prolonged (e.g., childhood sexual abuse), are typically associated with "massive denial, repression, [and] dissociation," resulting in amnesia for those experiences. Studies that find support for traumatic amnesia examined events that could be classified as Type II traumas, whereas those that find traumatic memories are vividly and clearly remembered examined events that could be classified as Type I traumas.

Second, *betrayal trauma theory* (BTT; DePrince et al., 2012; Freyd, 2008) proposes that when a child is traumatized by a close family member or caregiver, the child may be motivated to forget the trauma experience out of dependence upon the abuser. Through unawareness of the betrayal, the child is able to maintain an attachment to his or her caregiver and continue receiving the emotional and physical care that he or she requires (DePrince et al., 2012).

Although the precise mechanism responsible for the forgetting of traumatic memories remains unknown, and proponents of both sides continue the debate, researchers argue that different mechanisms may be under operation depending on the type, duration, and perpetrator of the trauma and on the developmental phase during which the trauma occurred (Lindsay & Read, 2001). Eventual recovery of traumatic memories years after forgetting is often attributed to exposure to reminders of the trauma and to having emotions or sensations similar to those experienced at the time of the trauma (van der Kolk & Fisler, 1995; Whitfield, 1995).

Do False Memories Exist, and If So, Why Do They Arise?

It has also been well established, primarily through laboratory-based research, that false memories can be implanted (Loftus, 2003, 2005; Loftus & Davis, 2006; McNally, 2003). More specifically, this line of research indicates that memory can be influenced by leading questions and misinformation. A commonly utilized research paradigm is to have individuals view a simulated incident (e.g., a car accident or violent crime). Half the participants are then provided with misinformation about the incident (e.g., they are told that the car in the accident was a different color from that originally seen or that there was broken glass when there was none); the other half receive no such misinformation. Participants are then later asked to recall the original incident. Findings have revealed that many participants adopt and report the misinformation as their own memories of the event (Loftus, 2005; Loftus & Pickrell, 1995).

Likewise, Lindsay, Hagen, Read, Wade, and Garry (2004) conducted a review of eight studies that utilized a procedure called *familial informant false narrative procedure* and found that through the use of suggestion, many unsuspecting individuals were led to believe event histories that were not true: They developed pseudomemories. For example, they were provided with misinformation that as children they were victims of a vicious attack, were nearly drowned and had to be rescued, or were lost in a shopping mall. Of the 374 subjects who participated across studies, 31% were coded as having partial or complete false memories of events that never occurred. Individuals with complete false memories provided more evidence to suggest they believed the false events (Lindsay et al., 2004). Several criticisms have been lobbied against these false memory studies, including claims that they lack ecological validity and that their findings may not generalize to individuals who experienced significant traumatic events. Moreover, there is no evidence to date that "false memories" of abuse can be implanted in those with no history of trauma (Olio & Cornell, 1994). Despite these criticisms, this line of research provides compelling evidence that false memories can be implanted.

A prominent theory of how false memories occur is that the corroboration of misinformation by an authority figure strongly biases the memory formation process. Also, the time between exposure to the original event and the provision of misinformation can also influence memory retrieval, with a longer passage of time being associated with the inability to detect discrepancy between the original event and the misinformation (Loftus, 2005). Although findings support the existence of false memories, they do not, however, negate the existence or reliability of recovered memories (International Society for the Study of Trauma and Dissociation [ISSTD], 2011). Both types of memories are just as likely.

Points of Agreement

In summary, it is widely accepted in both the clinical and scientific communities that experiences of childhood maltreatment are generally well remembered. However, among a small subgroup of individuals exposed to trauma, memories for traumatic events can be forgotten and then later recovered. False memories do also exist. Thus, some recovered memories may be accurate or true, while other recovered memories may contain errors or be false (Brewin, 2007; Lindsay & Briere, 1997). However, the existence of false memories cannot be used to negate the existence of recovered memories. The precise mechanism responsible for the forgetting of traumatic memories remains unknown. Without corroborating information, however, it is impossible to determine whether a recovered memory is true or false (APA, 2013).

IS DISSOCIATIVE IDENTITY DISORDER A VALID DIAGNOSIS?

Dissociative Identity Disorder (DID), formerly known as Multiple Personality Disorder (MPD), is one of the most controversial diagnoses in the *Diagnostic and Statistical Manual of Mental Disorders, Fifth Edition* (*DSM-5*; APA, 2013). According to the *DSM-5*, DID is characterized by two main criteria: (1) disruption of identity characterized by *two or more distinct* personality states (often referred to as "alters" or "ego states") or an experience of possession, and (2) recurrent gaps in the recall of everyday events, important personal information, or traumatic events that are inconsistent with ordinary forgetting. This latter criterion reflects the degree to which dissociative amnesia pervades the individual's everyday experience. These symptoms must not be attributed to a medical condition or substance use, must cause clinically significant distress or impairment in the individual's social and occupational functioning, and should not be a broadly accepted cultural or religious practice (APA, 2013).

Although DID was once considered a rare disorder, with only 20 documented cases between 1944 and 1969, since the 1970s and 1980s there has been a significant increase in the number of individuals diagnosed with DID. There has also been a concomitant interest in understanding the etiology, assessment, and treatment of this disorder. Critics, who vigorously question the validity of DID, argue that the sudden increase in prevalence rates of DID is due to factors such as misdiagnosis and overdiagnosis of DID by a small segment of mental health clinicians who inadvertently induce the symptoms of DID in highly suggestible clients; sociocultural influences (e.g., media portrayals of

DID, such as *The Three Faces of Eve* and *Sybil*), which popularized and sensationalized the diagnosis; and conscious malingering by those attempting to avoid criminal prosecution (Kihlstrom, 2005; Lynn, Lilienfeld, Merckelbach, Giesbrecht, & van der Kloet, 2012; Piper & Merskey, 2004a, 2004b).

In contrast, supporters of DID argue that DID is a valid and reliable diagnosis documented across cultures, research teams, and methodologies and one that cannot be convincingly faked on psychological or neurobiological tests (Brand, McNary, Loewenstein, Kolos, & Barr, 2006; Brand & Chasson, 2014; Dalenberg et al., 2012; Reinders, Willemsen, Vos, den Boer, & Nijenhuis, 2012). What follows is a brief review of the key points of the controversy, which center on the etiology and treatment of dissociative identity disorder.

What Is the Etiology of DID?

Trauma Model. One of the most prominent and well-accepted etiological models of DID is the posttraumatic stress model (Gleaves, 1996; ISSTD, 2011). According to this theory, DID is viewed as a developmental psychopathological condition that develops as a result of exposure to severe and prolonged childhood traumatic experiences, particularly sexual and physical abuse. These traumatic experiences often occur within the context of a dysfunctional parent–child attachment relationship, which sets the stage for significant posttrauma pathology.

During and after exposure to high levels of psychological stress, the traumatized child defensively copes with these overwhelming experiences by dissociating or compartmentalizing ("splitting off") painful memories, thoughts, and feelings (ISSTD, 2011). These split-off aspects of the child's experience become consolidated into alternate personality states, each with different characteristics. In essence, the severely maltreated child, through a complex mental process, comes to believe that the trauma is happening to someone else, and hence the memories of such are disowned (Gillig, 2009). DID is typically seen as an adaptive response at the time to an extremely stressful situation, as full awareness and recollection of the situation would be even more traumatic or devastating. Evidence also suggests that dissociation has a strong neurobiological basis and may be automatically activated in response to a severe threat or attack (Brand, Lanius, Vermetten, Loewenstein, & Spiegel, 2012; Lanius et al., 2010).

Critics of the posttraumatic model assert there is insufficient evidence to support trauma as a causal factor in the development of DID (Kihlstrom, 2005; Lynn et al., 2012; Piper & Merskey, 2004a, 2004b). A main point of contention is that an association between trauma exposure and DID does not equal causation. Opponents argue that given the inability to know how many people exposed to trauma do *not* develop DID, one cannot definitively say that trauma is a primary and specific causative factor (Piper & Merskey, 2004a). They also point out the lack of independent corroboration for traumatic experiences. Furthermore, prevalence studies tend to be cross-sectional and lack documentation of the age, nature, and chronicity of the trauma experienced by individuals with DID, all of which limit the ability to make causal inferences about the role of trauma in the development of DID.

Finally, since the information gathered about trauma exposure is based on self-reports, these reports are subject to questions about the veracity of memories. Memory is inherently subject to errors because it is a reconstructive process, and may be influenced by a variety of cognitive and social factors (Traub, 2009). Thus, on the one hand, self-reported memories of trauma may be entirely accurate and true. However, on the other hand, self-reported memories may be distorted or false. Without objective corroboration of the trauma, some argue, there would be no way of knowing with certainty whether self-reported child maltreatment ever occurred (Kihlstrom, 2005; Lynn et al., 2012).

Advocates of the DID diagnosis, however, highlight that the symptoms, characteristics, and histories of individuals with DID have been documented across cultures, research teams, and methodologies (Dalenberg et al., 2012; Sar, 2011). For example, Sar (2011) conducted a review of several epidemiological studies conducted in the United States, Puerto Rico, Turkey, and the Netherlands and found prevalence rates of DID ranging from 0.4% to 14% in clinical and community samples, indicating that DID is a common mental health problem in the world. From 50% to 100% of the individuals diagnosed with DID also reported significant histories of childhood trauma (Dalenberg et al., 2012; Sar, 2011).

Furthermore, multiple studies have found corroboration or confirmation of abuse histories reported by those with DID (Coons, 1994; Gleaves, Hernandez, & Warner, 1999; Lewis, Yeager, Swica, Pincus, & Lewis, 1997). For example, Lewis et al. (1997) conducted a study of 12 murderers on death row who had been diagnosed with DID and found objective, verifiable evidence in medical and social services records, as well as corroboration by first-degree family members and close friends, of the severe physical and sexual abuse endured by these individuals. Additional studies conducted by Coons (1994) and Coons and Milstein (1986) found documented corroboration of child trauma history for child, adolescent, and adult patients with DID. Overall, these studies lend support to the link between self-report and objective measures of trauma exposure and dissociation in general and DID in particular.

Social–Cognitive Model. An alternative model of DID, the social–cognitive model, argues that DID is not a valid diagnosis but rather a social construction reinforced by cultural and therapeutic factors (Lilienfeld et al., 1999; Spanos, 1994). Also known as the fantasy model (Dalenberg et al., 2012), this model argues that media portrayals of DID, inadvertent therapist cueing (e.g., asking suggestive questions about the existence of alters and reinforcing expressions of DID symptoms), and other sociocultural expectations all combine to make a highly suggestible individual, with a tendency toward fantasy proneness, more susceptible to enacting or playing the role of someone with DID with false memories of abuse that did not occur (Lynn et al., 2012; Piper & Merskey, 2004a, 2004b).

Recent studies, however, suggest that DID is not linked to fantasy proneness. Dalenberg et al. (2012) conducted a comprehensive review of suggestibility studies and found no convincing evidence for a correlation between dissociation and suggestibility. In fact, effect sizes of the association between the two constructs were small (ranging from 1% to 3%), indicating that individuals with dissociative symptoms are no more likely to be susceptible to suggestion and to the production of false memories than those without dissociative pathology (Dalenberg et al., 2012). Furthermore, the general concern that DID can be successfully feigned by malingerers to avoid criminal punishment, or for factitious reasons (e.g., to take on the "sick role" in order to receive attention and sympathy), has been unfounded. Studies to date indicate it is not easy to convincingly fake DID (Brand et al., 2006; Brand & Chasson, 2014). For example, Brand et al. (2006) compared 20 patients clinically diagnosed with DID to 46 undergraduate students who were instructed to fake DID. Results revealed that the Structured Interview of Reported Symptoms (SIRS; Rogers, Bagby, & Dickens, 1992), a measure designed to detect malingering, was able to successfully differentiate those with simulated DID from those with genuine DID.

In another study, Brand and Chasson (2014) utilized the Minnesota Multiphasic Personality Inventory (MMPI-2) to compare 53 clinically diagnosed individuals with DID, 77 participants who were coached and instructed to simulate DID, and 67 participants who were uncoached but instructed to simulate DID. Results revealed the participants instructed to feign DID were not able to successfully do so, with the MMPI-2 successfully discriminating genuine DID from simulated DID.

Finally, Reinders et al. (2012) examined 10 high fantasy-prone controls and 8 low fantasy-prone controls who were instructed to fake two DID identity states while completing an autobiographical memory paradigm. Their psychophysiological responses and neural activation were recorded and compared to

11 patients with genuine DID who also completed the same paradigm. Results revealed that there were significant differences in neurobiological reactivity between individuals with genuine DID and high and low fantasy prone controls. The high and low fantasy controls were not able to successfully simulate DID identity states and thus did not produce previously discovered neurobiological states indicative of genuine DID. Taken together, these findings are inconsistent with the sociocognitive or fantasy model of DID and instead lend support to the idea that DID is not a condition that can be easily enacted based on suggestion or roleplay.

Does Treatment of DID Make Clients Worse?

Critics also argue that the treatments developed for DID are not empirically supported, are based on false assumptions about the etiology of DID (i.e., uncorroborated trauma), and in fact may make individuals diagnosed with DID worse off (Kihlstrom, 2005; Lilienfeld & Lambert, 2007). In contrast, proponents point to a growing body of peer-reviewed, cross-sectional, and longitudinal research that shows that DID patients do improve when the treatment provided is consistent with expert guidelines (Brand et al., 2009; Brand, Lanius, et al., 2012).

Expert guidelines for the treatment of DID recommend adherence to a phase-based oriented treatment encompassing (1) safety, stabilization, and symptom reduction; (2) working through and integrating traumatic memories and self-states; and (3) integration and rehabilitation (Brand, Lanius, et al., 2012; ISSTD, 2011). Brand, McNary, et al. (2012) conducted an international, prospective naturalistic study of the treatment of individuals with DID and dissociative disorder not otherwise specified (DDNOS) and found that at multiple follow-up time-points, both groups of patients showed significant reductions in DID and PTSD symptoms and displayed improvements in social, occupational, and life functioning. Moreover, therapists reported that their patients engaged in less self-destructive behaviors, improved their global functioning, and had fewer hospitalizations. This study provides strong preliminary evidence of the effectiveness of treatment for DID. Brand and colleagues (Brand, Lanius, et al., 2012; Brand, McNary, et al., 2012; Brand, Myrick, et al., 2012) argue that the most likely harm to befall DID patients is that there are not enough treatment providers who recognize and treat dissociative disorders, so these patients are likely to have considerable difficulty getting treatment that follows the expert consensus guidelines.

Summary

Despite the controversy surrounding DID, its validity and reliability as a diagnostic construct is generally well accepted, as evidenced by its inclusion in the *DSM-5* (APA, 2013). Several studies have objectively verified that individuals with DID do indeed have histories of severe childhood maltreatment, supporting the trauma model of DID. Research also shows that individuals with DID are *not* more suggestible than others and thus are not enacting a role based on therapist suggestions and are not more likely to report false memories. In fact, studies show that DID cannot be reliably and successfully faked. Psychological and neurobiological tests have been able to successfully differentiate those with genuine DID from those simulating DID.

Concerns about treatment making DID clients worse have been unfounded. New peer-reviewed research has shown that individuals with DID who received treatment consistent with expert guidelines improved significantly across all relevant spheres (i.e., reduction in symptoms and improvements in social and occupational functioning). Nevertheless, the lingering concerns regarding the validity of the diagnosis point to the need for continued education and research on this challenging condition.

REFERENCES

Allen, J. G., Fultz, J., Huntoon, J., & Brethour, J. R., Jr. (2002). Pathological dissociative taxon membership, absorption, and reported childhood trauma in women with trauma-related disorders. *Journal of Trauma & Dissociation, 3*, 89–110. doi:10.1300/J229v03n01_07

American Psychiatric Association. (1980). *Diagnostic and statistical manual of mental disorders* (3rd ed.). Washington, DC: Author.

American Psychiatric Association. (1997). *Diagnostic and statistical manual of mental disorders* (4th ed.). Washington, DC: Author.

American Psychiatric Association. (2000). *Diagnostic and statistical manual of mental disorders* (4th ed., text revision). Washington, DC: Author.

American Psychiatric Association. (2013). *Diagnostic and statistical manual of mental disorders* (5th ed.). Washington, DC: Author.

Brand, B., Classen, C. C., Lanius, R., Loewenstein, R. J., McNary, S. W., Pain, C., & Putnam, F. W. (2009). A naturalistic study of dissociative identity disorder and dissociative disorder not otherwise specified patients treated by community clinicians. *Psychological Trauma: Theory, Research, Practice, and Policy, 1*, 153–171. doi:10.1037/a0016210

Brand, B. L., & Chasson, G. S. (2014, March 17). Distinguishing simulated from genuine dissociative identity disorder on the MMPI-2. *Psychological Trauma: Theory, Research, Practice, and Policy.* Advance online publication. http://dx.doi.org/10.1037/a0035181

Brand, B. L., Lanius, R., Vermetten, E., Loewenstein, R. J., & Spiegel, D. (2012). Where are we going? An update on assessment, treatment, and neurobiological research in dissociative disorders as we move toward the *DSM-5*. *Journal of Trauma & Dissociation, 13*(1), 9–31.

Brand, B. L., McNary, S. W., Loewenstein, R. J., Kolos, A. C., & Barr, S. R. (2006). Assessment of genuine and simulated dissociative identity disorder on the Structured Interview of Reported Symptoms. *Journal of Trauma & Dissociation, 7*(1), 63–85.

Brand, B. L., McNary, S. W., Myrick, A. C., Classen, C. C., Lanius, R., Loewenstein, R. J., . . . Putnam, F. W. (2012). A longitudinal naturalistic study of patients with dissociative disorders treated by community clinicians. *Psychological Trauma: Theory, Research, Practice, and Policy, 5*(4), 301–308. doi:10.1037/a0027654

Brand, B. L., Myrick, A. C., Loewenstein, R. J., Classen, C. C., Lanius, R., McNary, S. W., . . . Putnam, F. W. (2012). A survey of practices and recommended treatment interventions among expert therapists treating patients with dissociative identity disorder and dissociative disorder not otherwise specified. *Psychological Trauma: Theory, Research, Practice, and Policy, 4*(5), 490. doi:10.1037/a0026487

Brewin, C. R. (2007). Remembering and forgetting. In M. J. Friedman, T. M. Keane, & P. A. Resick (Eds.), *Handbook of PTSD: Science and practice* (pp. 116–124). New York, NY: Guilford Press.

Bryant, R. A. (2012). Simplifying complex PTSD: Comment on Resick et al. (2012). *Journal of Traumatic Stress, 25*(3), 252–253. doi:10.1002/jts.21696

Cloitre, M., Courtois, C. A., Charuvastra, A., Carapezza, R., Stolbach, B. C., & Green, B. L. (2011). Treatment of complex PTSD: Results of the ISTSS expert clinician survey on best practices. *Journal of Traumatic Stress, 24*(6), 615–627. doi:10.1002/jts.20697

Colangelo, J. J. (2009). The recovered memory controversy: A representative case study. *Journal of Child Sexual Abuse, 18*(1), 103–121. doi:10.1080/10538710802584601.

Coons, P. M. (1994). Confirmation of childhood abuse in child and adolescent cases of multiple personality disorder and dissociative disorder not otherwise specified. *The Journal of Nervous and Mental Disease, 182*(8), 461–464.

Coons, P. M., & Milstein, V. (1986). Psychosexual disturbances in multiple personality: Characteristics, etiology, and treatment. *Journal of Clinical Psychiatry, 47*, 106–110.

Courtois, C. A. (2004). Complex trauma, complex reactions: Assessment and treatment. *Psychotherapy: Theory, Research, Practice, Training, 41*, 412–425.

Courtois, C. A., & Ford, J. D. (2009). *Treating complex traumatic stress disorders: An evidence-based guide*. New York, NY: Guilford Press.

Courtois, C. A., & Ford, J. D. (2012). *Treatment of complex trauma: A sequenced, relationship-based approach*. New York, NY: Guilford Press.

Dalenberg, C. J. (1996). Accuracy, timing and circumstances of disclosure in therapy of recovered and continuous memories of abuse. *Journal of Psychiatry & Law, 24*, 229–275.

Dalenberg, C. (2006). Recovered memory and the Daubert Criteria recovered memory as professionally tested, peer reviewed, and accepted in the relevant scientific community. *Trauma, Violence, & Abuse, 7*(4), 274–310. doi:10.1177/1524838006294572

Dalenberg, C. J., Brand, B. L., Gleaves, D. H., Dorahy, M. J., Loewenstein, R. J., Cardeña, E., . . . Spiegel, D. (2012). Evaluation of the evidence for the trauma and fantasy models of dissociation. *Psychological Bulletin, 138*(3), 550. doi:10.1037/a0027447

Dammeyer, M. D., Nightingale, N. N., & McCoy, M. L. (1997). Repressed memory and other controversial origins of sexual abuse allegations: Beliefs among psychologists and clinical social workers. *Child Maltreatment, 2*(3), 252–263. doi:10.1177/1077559597002003007

DePrince, A. P., Brown, L. S., Cheit, R. E., Freyd, J. J., Gold, S. N., Pezdek, K., & Quina, K. (2012). Motivated forgetting and mis-remembering: Perspectives from betrayal trauma theory. In R. F. Belli (Ed.), *True and false recovered memories: Toward a reconciliation of the debate* (pp. 193–242). New York, NY: Springer.

Ford, J. D. (1999). PTSD and disorders of extreme stress following war zone military trauma: Comorbid but distinct syndromes? *Journal of Consulting and Clinical Psychology, 67*, 3–12.

Freud, S. (1915/1957). Repression. In J. Stravhey (Ed.), *The standard edition of the complete psychological works of Sigmund Freud* (Vol. 14, pp. 146–158). London: Hogarth Press.

Freyd, J. J. (2008). Betrayal trauma. In G. Reyes & J. D. Ford (Eds.), *Encyclopedia of psychological trauma* (p. 76). New York, NY: John Wiley & Sons.

Gillig, P. M. (2009). Dissociative identity disorder: A controversial diagnosis. *Psychiatry (Edgmont), 6*(3), 24–29.

Gleaves, D. H. (1996). The sociocognitive model of dissociative identity disorder: A reexamination of the evidence. *Psychological Bulletin, 120*(1), 42. doi:10.1037/0033-2909.120.1.42

Gleaves, D. H., Hernandez, E., & Warner, M. S. (1999). Corroborating premorbid dissociative symptomatology in dissociative identity disorder. *Professional Psychology: Research and Practice, 30*(4), 341–345. doi:10.1037/0735-7028.30.4.341

Goodman, G. S., Ghetti, S., Quas, J. A., Edelstein, R. S., Alexander, K. W., Redlich, A. D., . . . Jones, D. P. (2003). A prospective study of memory for child sexual abuse: New findings relevant to the repressed-memory controversy. *Psychological Science, 14*(2), 113–118. doi:10.1111/1467-9280.01428

Goodman, G. S., Quas, J. A., & Ogle, C. M. (2010). Child maltreatment and memory. *Annual Review of Psychology, 61*, 325–351. doi:10.1146/annurev.psych.093008.100403

Herman, J. L. (1992). Complex PTSD: A syndrome in survivors of prolonged and repeated trauma. *Journal of Traumatic Stress, 5*(3), 377–391.

International Society for the Study of Trauma and Dissociation. (2011). Guidelines for treating dissociative identity disorder in adults, third revision: Summary version. *Journal of Trauma and Dissociation, 12*, 188–212. doi:10.1080/15299732.2011.537248

Janet, P. (1889). *Psychological automatisms.* Paris: Alcan.

Keane, T. M., & Najavits, L. M. (2013). Interview: Does complex trauma exist? A "long view" based on science and service in the trauma field. *Journal of Clinical Psychology, 69*, 510–515. doi: 10.1002/jclp.21991

Kihlstrom, J. F. (2005). Dissociative disorders. *Annual Review of Clinical Psychology, 1*, 227–253. doi:10.1146/annurev.clinpsy.1.102803.143925

Kihlstrom, J. F., McNally, R. J., Loftus, E. F., & Pope, H. G., Jr. (2005). The problem of child sexual abuse. *Science, 309*, 1182–1185.

Lanius, R. A., Vermetten, E., Loewenstein, R. J., Brand, B., Schmahl, C., Bremner, J. D., & Spiegel, D. (2010). Emotion modulation in PTSD: Clinical and neurobiological evidence for a dissociative subtype. *The American Journal of Psychiatry, 167*(6), 640. doi:10.1176/appi.ajp.2009.09081168

Layton, B., & Krikorian, R. (2002). Memory mechanisms in post-traumatic stress disorder. *The Journal of Neuropsychiatry and Clinical Neurosciences, 14*(3), 254–261. doi:10.1176/appi.neuropsych.14.3.254

Lewis, D. O., Yeager, C. A., Swica, Y., Pincus, J. H., & Lewis, M. (1997). Objective documentation of child abuse and dissociation in 12 murderers with dissociative identity disorder. *American Journal of Psychiatry, 154*(12), 1703–1710.

Lewis, K. L., & Grenyer, B. F. (2009). Borderline personality or complex posttraumatic stress disorder? An update on the controversy. *Harvard Review of Psychiatry, 17*(5), 322–328. doi:10.3109/10673220903271848

Lilienfeld, S. O., Kirsch, I., Sarbin, T. R., Lynn, S. J., Chaves, J. F., Ganaway, G. K., & Powell, R. A. (1999). Dissociative identity disorder and the sociocognitive model: Recalling the lessons of the past. *Psychological Bulletin, 125*(5), 507–523.

Lilienfeld, S. O., & Lambert, K. (2007). Brain stains: Traumatic therapies can have long-lasting effects on mental health. *Scientific American Mind, 18*(5), 46–53.

Lindsay, D. S., & Briere, J. (1997). The controversy regarding recovered memories of childhood sexual abuse: Pitfalls, bridges, and future directions. *Journal of Interpersonal Violence, 12*, 631–647.

Lindsay, D. S., Hagen, L., Read, J. D., Wade, K. A., & Garry, M. (2004). True photographs and false memories. *Psychological Science, 15*, 149–154.

Lindsay, D. S., & Read, J. D. (2001). The recovered memories controversy: Where do we go from here? In G. M. Davies & T. Dagleish (Eds.), *Recovered memories: Seeking the middle ground* (pp. 71–94). West Sussex, England: John Wiley & Sons.

Loftus, E., & Ketcham, K. (1994). *The myth of repressed memory: False memories and allegations of sexual abuse.* New York, NY: St. Martin's Press.

Loftus, E. F. (2003). Make-believe memories. *American Psychologist, 58*(11), 867.

Loftus, E. F. (2005). Planting misinformation in the human mind: A 30-year investigation of the malleability of memory. *Learning & Memory, 12*(4), 361–366.

Loftus, E. F., & Davis, D. (2006). Recovered memories. *Annual Review of Clinical Psychology, 2*, 469–498.

Loftus, E. F., Joslyn, S., & Polage, D. (1998). Repression: A mistaken impression? *Development and Psychopathology, 10*, 781–792.

Loftus, E. F., & Pickrell, J. E. (1995). The formation of false memories. *Psychiatric Annals, 25*, 720–725.

Luxenberg, T., Spinazzola, J., & van der Kolk, B. A. (2001). Complex trauma and disorders of extreme stress (DESNOS) diagnosis, part 1: Assessment. *Directions in Psychiatry, 21*(25), 373–392.

Lynn, S. J., Lilienfeld, S. O., Merckelbach, H., Giesbrecht, T., & van der Kloet, D. (2012). Dissociation and dissociative disorders: Challenging conventional wisdom. *Current Directions in Psychological Science, 21*(1), 48–53.

McNally, R. J. (2003). Progress and controversy in the study of posttraumatic stress disorder. *Annual Review of Psychology, 54*(1), 229–252.

McNally, R. J., & Geraerts, E. (2009). A new solution to the recovered memory debate. *Perspectives on Psychological Science, 4*(2), 126–134.

Ofshe, R., & Watters, E. (1994). *Making monsters: False memories, psychotherapy, and sexual hysteria.* New York, NY: Charles Scribner and Sons.

Olio, K. A., & Cornell, W. F. (1994). Making meaning not monsters: Reflections on the delayed memory controversy. *Journal of Child Sexual Abuse, 3*, 77–94.

Pelcovitz, D., Van der Kolk, B. A., Roth, S., Mandel, F., Kaplan, S., & Resick, P. (1997). Development of a criteria set and a structured interview for disorders of extreme stress (SIDES). *Journal of Traumatic Stress, 10*(1), 3–16.

Piper, A., & Merskey, H. (2004a). The persistence of folly: A critical examination of dissociative identity disorder. Part I: The excesses of an improbable concept. *Canadian Journal of Psychiatry, 49,* 592–600.

Piper, A., & Merskey, H. (2004b). The persistence of folly: Critical examination of dissociative identity disorder. Part II: The defence and decline of multiple personality or dissociative identity disorder. *Canadian Journal of Psychiatry, 49*(10), 678–683.

Reinders, A. S., Willemsen, A. T., Vos, H. P., den Boer, J. A., & Nijenhuis, E. R. (2012). Fact or factitious? A psychobiological study of authentic and simulated dissociative identity states. *PloS One, 7*(6), e39279. doi:10.1371/journal.pone.0039279

Resick, P. A., Bovin, M. J., Calloway, A. L., Dick, A. M., King, M. W., Mitchell, K. S., . . . Wolf, E. J. (2012). A critical evaluation of the complex PTSD literature: Implications for DSM-5. *Journal of Traumatic Stress, 25,* 241–251.

Rogers, R., Bagby, R. M., & Dickens, S. E. (1992). *SIRS, Structured Interview of Reported Symptoms: Professional manual.* Lutz, FL: Psychological Assessment Resources.

Sar, V. (2011). Epidemiology of dissociative disorders: An overview. *Epidemiology Research International,* 1–9. doi:10.1155/2011/404538

Scoboria, A., Ford, J., Lin, H. J., & Frisman, L. (2008). Exploratory and confirmatory factor analyses of the structured interview for disorders of extreme stress. *Assessment, 15*(4), 404–425. doi:10.1177/1073191108319005

Shobe, K. K., & Kihlstrom, J. F. (1997). Is traumatic memory special? *Current Directions in Psychological Science, 6*(3), 70–74.

Skinner, A. E. G. (2001). Recovered memories of abuse: The effects on the individual. In G. M. Davies & T. Dalgleish (Eds.), *Recovered memories: Seeking the middle ground* (pp. 35–49). West Sussex, England: John Wiley & Sons Ltd.

Spanos, N. P. (1994). Multiple identity enactments and multiple personality disorder: A sociocognitive perspective. *Psychological Bulletin, 116*(1), 143.

Straker, G., Watson, D., & Robinson, T. (2002). Trauma and disconnection: A trans-theoretical approach. *International Journal of Psychotherapy, 7*(2), 145–158. doi:10.1080/1356908021000016828

Terr, L. (1994). *Unchained memories: True stories of traumatic memory loss.* New York, NY: Basic Books.

Traub, C. M. (2009). Defending a diagnostic pariah: Validating the categorisation of dissociative identity disorder. *South African Journal of Psychology, 39*(3), 347–356. doi:10.1177/008124630903900309

van der Kolk, B. A. (1994). The body keeps the score: Memory and the evolving psychobiology of posttraumatic stress. *Harvard Review of Psychiatry, 1*(5), 253–265.

van der Kolk, B. A. (2002). Assessment and treatment of complex PTSD. In R. Yehuda (Ed.), *Treating trauma survivors with PTSD* (pp. 127–156). Washington, DC: American Psychiatric Publishing.

van der Kolk, B. A., & Fisler, R. (1995). Dissociation and the fragmentary nature of traumatic memories: Overview and exploratory study. *Journal of Traumatic Stress, 8*(4), 505–525. doi:10.1002/jts.2490080402

van der Kolk, B. A., Roth, S., Pelcovitz, D., Sunday, S., & Spinazzola, J. (2005). Disorders of extreme stress: The empirical foundation of a complex adaptation to trauma. *Journal of Traumatic Stress, 18*(5), 389–399. doi:10.1002/jts.20047

van der Kolk, B. A., & van der Hart, O. (1991). The intrusive past: The flexibility of memory and the engraving of trauma. *American Imago, 48*, 425–454.

Whitfield, C. L. (1995). *Memory and abuse: Remembering and healing the effects of trauma.* Deerfield Beach, FL: Health Communications.

Widom, C. S., & Morris, S. (1997). Accuracy of adult recollections of childhood victimization, part 2: Childhood sexual abuse. *Psychological Assessment, 9*(1), 34. doi:10.1037/1040-3590.9.1.34

Williams, L. (1994). Recall of childhood trauma: A prospective study of women's memories of child sexual abuse. *Journal of Consulting and Clinical Psychology, 62*(6), 1167–1176. doi:10.1037/0022-006X.62.6.1167

Williams, L. M. (1995). Recovered memories of abuse in women with documented child sexual victimization histories. *Journal of Traumatic Stress, 8*(4), 649–673.

Posttraumatic Growth

The pain individuals experience from [trauma] should not be minimized. Yet, it does not have to be the centerpiece of one's identity . . . most survivors display a stunning capacity for survival and perseverance. Growth and pain . . . are not necessarily mutually exclusive, but instead are inextricably linked in recovery from trauma.
—Anderson, Renner, and Danis, 2012, p. 1281

n March 6, 1987, the *Herald of Free Enterprise*, a passenger ship with 545 people on board, left Zeebrugge, Belgium, on its way to Dover, England. Thirty minutes into the trip, disaster struck. A bow door had been left open, allowing water to flood the car decks. Once flooded below, the ship capsized in less than a minute, instantly plunging the passengers and crew into the dark, icy water. One hundred ninety-three passengers died that night, in what would eventually be called the worst maritime accident of the 20th century.

Stephen Joseph, then a graduate student in clinical psychology at the Institute of Psychiatry in London, spent the next 3 years studying the survivors. As expected, many had symptoms of posttraumatic stress (PTS): sleep problems, depression, and use of drugs and alcohol to help them cope. But that wasn't the whole story. Three years after the disaster, almost half—43%—of the survivors said their lives were *better* since the disaster. It contradicted everything Joseph thought he knew about trauma, as he describes in his book *What Doesn't Kill Us: The New Psychology of Posttraumatic Growth*.

WHAT IS POSTTRAUMATIC GROWTH?

Posttraumatic growth (PTG) refers to positive psychological changes in the wake of traumatic or highly challenging life events. The person has survived the event and has improved in some significant ways that he or she views as meaningful. These changes do not mean an absence of struggle with the traumatic event and the ensuing crisis (Tedeschi & Calhoun, 2004). Growth does not occur as a direct result of trauma. Rather, it is the individual's struggle with the new reality in the aftermath of trauma that is crucial in determining whether posttraumatic growth occurs.

While growth following trauma is a relatively new area of study within psychology, it is a construct that has actually been around for a long time. PTG is part of many spiritual and religious traditions and is a common theme in literature and philosophy. In ancient times, and in current research, it is often the people who experience the most PTS symptoms who also experience the most posttraumatic growth (Joseph, 2011; Tedeschi & Calhoun, 2004). Indeed, significant distress may be necessary for growth to occur.

For example, a study of 55 psychiatric inpatients with refugee backgrounds found that PTG was related to lower levels of depression (Teodorescu et al., 2012). Most of these refugees had been multiply traumatized with events, such as imprisonment in concentration camps, torture, or repeated rape. As a consequence, they suffered from symptoms of PTS for years after their resettlement in their new country. In spite of this, some reported positive changes. In this study, a hierarchical regression model included depressive symptoms, PTS, PTG, and unemployment status. There was a medium-to-large inverse correlation between PTG and depressive symptoms. This model accounted for 56% of the total variance in mental health. PTG made the strongest contribution to the model. In contrast, unemployment, weak social network, and poor social integration were negatively related to both PTG and quality of life and positively associated with more symptoms of psychopathology.

A recent study of 197 ministerial employees present at the Oslo bombing also examined the link between level of trauma exposure and growth (Blix, Hansen, Birkeland, Nissen, & Heir, 2013). The bombing occurred in 2011 when a lone terrorist launched an attack against the government, exploding a car bomb near the offices of the prime minister and later that day opening fire at a day camp run by the Labour Party. Seventy-seven people died in the two attacks. In the study, greater growth was associated with higher levels of both trauma exposure and PTS. Many of the survivors who reported high PTG also reported high levels of impairment in their daily lives. Impairment was measured on the Work and Social Adjustment Scale, which asks therapy clients to rate their level of impairment—because of the way they feel—at work, in managing their household, in social and private leisure activities, and in relationships. Even though the group with high PTG reported significant impairment in their daily lives, they also reported higher levels of life satisfaction. The authors concluded that we should not judge PTG as a solely negative or positive phenomenon. Recovery from traumatic events is complex, as is the phenomenon of PTG.

Survivors' own narratives complement quantitative findings well and illustrate an uncanny self-awareness inherent to PTG. For example, Lucie (not her real name) describes her process of recovery from a very violent marriage. Her journey toward recovery began after a particularly vicious marital rape and severe beating. Following those two events, she developed severe PTSD, during which time she realized that she had been minimizing the suffering that she had been experiencing for years:

> That whole time I could not get over being so aghast that I was watching myself in a really, really, REALLY bad, I mean BAD Lifetime Movie Event whose script even a famous actress would turn down! . . .

After that, I was amazed to realize I covered pretty much every *DSM* symptom of PTSD in short order. One that still fascinates me, even to this day, is the "zombie" stage. I still didn't think it was all that bad or qualitatively different/abnormal from other people's marital fights, so when my stepmom one day happened to call and ask me how things were going, and I described these two horrific events in response, I was baffled when she then showed up at my doorstep the next day (in Philadelphia! from Seattle!). I think I even said something like, "What are you doing here? Don't you have to be at work?" and was genuinely confused as to why in the world she thought she needed to be there.

My healing and growth started with her incredibly loving support and continued with really committing myself to LOTS of good therapy (alone, with the kids, the kids alone), yoga, mindfulness work, prayer, journaling, all of which my stepmom thankfully urged me to keep doing. Interesting to me, in hindsight, is how she drew upon her professional expertise in birth trauma to support my transition back to health. Thankfully, my own three births had been the opposite of traumatic; in fact her support reminded me of my midwives back then, and especially of my doula for my third birth—I'll always wonder if those midwives knew how much I needed those three amazing births to be my beacons of joy in the dark of that marriage.

Throughout this healing I was struck by how similar it is to "doula-ing" someone through a drug-free birth: accepting and welcoming the pain, identifying the stages, being empowered to decide for yourself how to proceed at each juncture, learning to listen to and trust your body, breathing, being patient, forgiving, recognizing what is your job/responsibility and what is not, letting go of what others think about you and your decisions, staying present and mindful, keeping away from being too "empirical," or analyzing what's happening and assigning any qualitative judgment of whether what's happening is good or bad, TRUSTING there is a beautiful outcome at the end that makes it all worth it, no matter how preposterous that may seem in the meantime, knowing that once that concrete event comes (the actual birth, the divorce, the new locks on the doors, whatever), nothing will ever again be like it was before, which is a very, very good thing, and realizing that eventually, once that concrete event is in the distant past, you will only be able to believe that your life wasn't always as tremendously beautiful and amazing as it is now if you sit with the (albeit still very painful, but real and okay, and conquered) memories that only you have of what it was like before, and when you do, you'll be so relieved and proud of how far you've come.

. . . So yeah, there's still a lot of shite and pain and work, but . . . I see the incredible relationship I have with my kids and glimmers of healing in them every day, I know deeply what a relief it is to be able to sleep at night, eat regularly, and I've almost entirely replaced my default setting of "terrified" that used to rule my days and make my stomach lurch every time I had to interact with him, respond (or ignore!) a harassing email or text, with a default to breathe, accept, appreciate, and go on as best I can. This puts the work still to come in its proper perspective—gone is the black hole vortex of pain; it's been replaced by a long and twisty, but light-filled footpath. It's all good.

Another huge part of my growth was learning to stand up to the voice in my head, replacing it with a rotating cast of mantras (which have now become so routine they are running jokes with the kids!), including

- Everything always works out.
- All is well.
- This, too, shall pass, whether you like it or not.
- Breathing is good.
- Love is not a bank! (We had to undo years of creepy transactional behavior, like "I was nice for 5 days straight, you know!" or "I did this for you, so now you owe me x." or "If you don't do x, then there's no way I'm doing y." or "That's exactly how you treat me all the time!")

And we laugh a LOT.

PTG VERSUS RESILIENCE

Researchers have also examined the relationship between resilience and growth. Is PTG a type of resilience? Does resilience help in the development of PTG? Resilience is defined as exposure to traumatic events without developing psychopathology. Some studies have shown an inverse relationship between PTG and resilience, with less psychological growth for people who are highly resilient (Tedeschi & McNally, 2011). Highly resilient individuals are less likely to struggle with trauma and are therefore less likely to experience the positive changes that proceed from the struggle.

One recent study of 2,908 adolescents exposed to terror, and 588 citizens and military after the second Lebanon war, found that PTG and resilience were inversely related (Levine, Laufer, Stein, Hamama-Raz, & Solomon, 2009). Those with the highest resilience had the lowest PTG. The authors noted that both constructs are related to better mental health—but they are inversely related. In the sample of 588 citizens, those with the highest PTG were those who had the highest levels of PTSD. Their findings suggest that high resilience leaves little room for PTG.

HOW GROWTH HAPPENS: ASSUMPTIONS SHATTERED BY TRAUMATIC EVENTS

Traumatic events often provoke an existential crisis and can profoundly change trauma survivors' views of the world. Before tragedy strikes, people often make unconscious assumptions about the way the world works. Traumatic events often challenge some of their deepest beliefs about the world and their place in it. Janoff-Bulman (1992) describes this as a "shattering of our assumptions" about the world. Growth occurs when we grapple with these assumptions, find meaning in the event, and come to terms with the new, irreversible reality that follows. These assumptions include the following.

The World Is Benevolent

The first assumption that is shattered by trauma is that the world is benevolent. Americans often believe this, largely because we are relatively sheltered from the danger that people in other parts of the world face on a daily basis. Because of this, we underestimate our risk of misfortune. We "know," for example, that people get cancer or heart disease or are victims of crime or have car accidents, but we often assume that somehow these events will not happen to us. Unfortunately, even living in this privileged environment does not shield us from tragedy. It could be a vicious street crime, car accident, sexual assault, or diagnosis of a life-threatening illness: Such events show us quite clearly that the world is not always benevolent, that it can in fact be a dangerous place.

The World Is Meaningful

Our second assumption is that the world is meaningful, controllable, predictable, and just. Good things happen to good people. As long as we are "good," bad things will not happen to us. We try to control as much as we can. We exercise, eat well, drive with our seat belts on, and avoid risky behaviors. These are all good things to do. But the reality is that bad things happen to good people—all the time. And these events are frequently random.

We Are Decent and Worthy

The third assumption is that we tend to view ourselves in a positive light. We assume that we are decent and worthy, so when bad things happen, we wonder: "What did I do to deserve this?" Psychologist Tom Greening, at the recent meetings of the American

Psychological Association, described his work with veterans, many of whom were Christians. The events these soldiers experienced challenged their beliefs in some fundamental ways. They wondered how a loving God can allow so much suffering and pain, for themselves or others. Some lost their faith as a result. For these veterans, Greening found that traditional treatments for PTSD were only partially effective. Recovery only happened once the soldiers grappled with their beliefs and the events that they had experienced and came to terms with them.

MAKING MEANING OF THE EVENT

Research on PTG demonstrates that growth in the midst of crisis is possible, but not everyone will experience it (Tedeschi & Calhoun, 2004). Survivors need to make sense of the event. These individuals no longer view the world as just, but rather as random and unjust. They make sense of the event by assimilating the new trauma-related meaning into their existing worldviews: either by changing the meaning of the event or by changing their worldview (Duran, 2013). Rationalizing or making sense of the event reduces their anxiety and leads to better adjustment.

A key to PTG is what psychologists describe as "constructing a cohesive narrative" about what happened. It has to do with the stories we tell ourselves about what we have experienced. What increases the likelihood of PTG is the willingness of the person to reflectively "ruminate" over elements of the event to repair and restructure his or her understanding of the world (Joseph, 2011). Perceived growth is thought to arise when people try to make sense of what happened and cope with their emotional reactions (Blix et al., 2013). This process allows trauma survivors to reflect on their lives, observe new strengths, and find meaning in the event, often by seeing "the bigger picture."

In a recent study, Duran (2013) compiled a narrative synthesis of 35 studies of childhood cancer survivors. This analysis contained the results of 20 quantitative, 12 qualitative, and 3 mixed studies and included 1,115·parents and 159 healthy siblings. Duran identified five themes related to PTG. Meaning-making was one of the themes (Duran, 2013), and included the process of trying to understand a traumatic event and restore some understanding of it into a global system that had been disrupted or violated. In this study, mothers reported their first reaction to their child's cancer diagnosis: "How could this be possible?" or "Why does God let anything like this happen?" (p. 7). There were three types of meaning-making: (1) religious meaning-making (God planned this and had a purpose for it), (2) meaning-making through benefit finding (they received many positives, such as close friendships), and (3) meaning-making through being "special." (If they survived, it was because they were special, but not in a religious sense.)

Anderson and colleagues (2012) suggest the following questions to assist survivors who seek answers to the question, "Why me?"

- What lessons have you learned from enduring suffering? Have you seen positive changes in yourself, relationships with others, and the beyond (e.g., God, a higher power, or the universe)?
- Have you found meaning in your suffering? Do you think your suffering had some kind of purpose?
- Does your suffering provide you with a greater life purpose (e.g., breaking the cycle of violence, wanting to make a difference for others)?
- Have you ever felt connected to something beyond yourself (e.g., God, a higher power, or the universe)? Does this connection give you a sense of meaning or purpose in life? (pp. 1295–1296)

WHAT IS THE LIVED EXPERIENCE OF PTG?

Making meaning of the traumatic event was the first theme Duran (2013) identified in her summary of findings with survivors of childhood cancer. There were four others, and these outline the ways that survivors say that their lives have changed for the better as the result of experiencing trauma.

The second theme was a deeper appreciation of life (Duran, 2013). Survivors acquired a new philosophy of life and developed an appreciation of life in the here and now. They made a commitment to live life consciously and to the fullest extent possible. Their changed view of life also included new values and life priorities and learning to be less materialistic. It also guided how they chose friends.

The third theme is greater self-knowledge (Duran, 2013). The majority of the cancer survivors pointed to a weakness they overcame and to how their experiences enhanced their self-improvement. They also noted an increased sense of personal strength ("what doesn't kill you makes you stronger"). Adults who had had cancer as children also reported that they grew up a little faster as a result of their experiences.

The fourth theme was a greater sense of closeness and family togetherness (Duran, 2013). Families that were cohesive to begin with reported that their children's cancer had a positive effect on their family life and improved their families' sense of togetherness. They now place greater emphasis on their family relationships. This was especially true for religious families; these families believed that their children's survival was a family accomplishment.

The final theme was a desire to give back (Duran, 2013). Most of the cancer survivors, and a high percentage of their mothers, wanted to "give back" to society because their children had survived cancer. They acknowledged the help and support that they received when they needed it and now wanted to provide that care for others. Many had become peer counselors working with newly diagnosed patients.

Themes Identified by the PTG Inventory

The themes that patients in Duran's (2013) study identified are quite similar to those that Tedeschi and Calhoun (1996) identified using the Posttraumatic Growth Inventory, a 21-item instrument that assesses positive outcomes in people who have experienced traumatic events. Tedeschi and Calhoun identified five domains or factors within the larger construct of PTG. The five factors include relating to others (greater intimacy and compassion for others), new possibilities (new roles and new people), personal strength (feeling personally stronger), spiritual change (being more connected spiritually), and a deeper appreciation of life (Tedeschi & Calhoun, 2004).

INDIVIDUAL DIFFERENCES IN PTG

What makes growth more likely in some individuals and less likely in others? A recent review noted that PTG was related to optimism, social support, spirituality, acceptance coping, reappraisal coping, and religious coping (Meyerson, Grant, Carter, & Kilmer, 2011). Age and gender moderated coping–PTG. Religious coping was beneficial for older individuals and women. Females reported more PTG than males, and the percentage of females who experienced PTG increased as they got older.

A study of 148 severely traumatized youth (mean age 15) found that PTG could occur in youth with patterns similar to those seen in adults (Glad, Jensen, Holt, & Ormhaug, 2013). However, the rates of PTG pretreatment were low. The main themes the youth identified were personal growth, relational growth, and greater maturity and wisdom. They felt more self-confident, independent, and self-protective. They had more self-knowledge and greater courage. Trauma improved their interpersonal relationships and made them closer. It also showed the teens that they needed other people, and it allowed them to show greater empathy and more compassion for others. Treatment resulted in greater PTG, but PTG was not related to a decrease in posttraumatic symptoms. In addition, older youth were more likely than younger youth in the sample to experience PTG.

A review of 24 studies of PTSD in breast cancer patients found that a relatively small percentage of women experienced PTSD as a result of their diagnosis, but a majority experienced PTG (Koutrouli, Anagnostopoulos, & Potamianos, 2012). Those who experienced PTG ranged from 83% to 98% in different studies. There were a number of factors that predicted PTG. These included age, education, economic status, subjective appraisal of the threat of the disease, treatment, support from significant others, and positive coping strategies. Younger patients experienced more growth, as did patients with less education, women who were racial/ethnic minorities, and those with higher incomes. Support specific to overcoming adversity was related to growth, while social support, in general, was not. Quality of the marital relationship was either related to PTG or not related at all. These findings suggest that marital quality might be an outcome of growth rather than a contributor to it. Positive coping included active adaptive coping, religious coping, and positive reappraisal.

Most studies of women formerly in abusive relationships have focused on their posttraumatic symptoms and the many negative life changes that happened after the women left their abusive relationships. A mixed-methods study examining PTG among 37 women who had previously been in abusive relationships found that both social support and spirituality helped them recover and grow (Anderson et al., 2012). At the time of the interview, most were asymptomatic for PTSD, despite having lived in abusive relationships for a minimum of 5 years. The symptoms they experienced most often included trouble falling asleep, feeling upset by reminders, and feeling on guard. PTSD was more common in women with a history of childhood abuse.

The participants showed high levels of resilience, including personal competence, trust in their instincts, positive acceptance of change, secure relationships, control, and spirituality (Anderson et al., 2012). Higher resilience scores were related to lower PTSD scores. Some of the statements with the highest relationships to PTG were "I have at least one close and secure relationship which helps me when I am stressed" and "I take pride in my achievements."

Spirituality was also important: "When there are no clear solutions to my problems, sometimes fate or God can help." The fourth-highest ranking statement was "Good or bad, I believe that most things happen for a reason." In the qualitative analysis of this same data set, 23 of 31 participants indicated that God saved their lives and was a source of love and protection, also providing strength and hope (Anderson et al., 2012).

Eight of the women expressed that although there were violent episodes, their view of God was more negative, as they felt God had failed to protect them. However, as they worked through their crises, their recovery allowed them to change their previously held views of God as neglectful and uncaring. Spiritual communities aided in their recovery by providing emotional support, a sense of belonging, security, practical assistance, mentoring, and companionship. Some did receive unhelpful advice, however, from their religious communities, such as pressure to "just forgive" their abuser and or stay in their marriages (Anderson et al., 2012).

The social support these women received was from informal networks of family, friends, and supportive employers (Anderson et al., 2012). They were also able to access formal networks of support, including domestic violence services and mental health counseling. A few mentioned mental health counselors who were not helpful: These counselors tried to blame the victim for the abuse or simply did not know how to respond. Some of the women in the study continued to exhibit signs of psychopathology even when they also showed signs of resilience, demonstrating that resilience and psychopathology are not necessarily mutually exclusive.

Another recent study also found that type of religious belief made a difference in mothers' recovery after Hurricane Katrina (Chan & Rhodes, 2013). This sample included 386 low-income mothers 1 year and 4 years after the storm. The researchers looked at both positive and negative religious coping. Positive religious coping included looking for God's strength and support, feeling as if God might be trying to strengthen them through this situation, and asking God to help them overcome their bitterness. In contrast, negative religious coping included indicating that Satan was responsible for their situation, feeling as if God had abandoned them, and feeling as if God were punishing them for their sins. In previous studies, negative religious coping was associated with mental health problems, including depression.

As predicted, positive religious coping was associated with PTG, and an increase in religiosity pre- and postdisaster influenced PTG through positive religious coping (Chan & Rhodes, 2013). In contrast, negative religious coping was associated with psychological distress, but not posttraumatic symptoms. They found that neither social support nor optimism was related to posttraumatic symptoms and speculated that religious coping may have fueled the association among support, optimism, and disaster outcomes in previous studies.

PATHWAYS TO PTG

Paul Wong, president of the International Network on Personal Meaning, writes that even in the best of times, the pathway to personal growth is challenging. After trauma, it is even more challenging. "The pathways to PTG begin with brokenness and deficits. Before growth can take place, one needs to choose to embark on the long journey of recovery, to restore shattered assumptions, regain confidence, and find healing at physical, emotional, and spiritual levels. The following pathways to PTG are based in both the research and clinical literature" (Wong, 2003).

(1) Acceptance

You no longer live in denial or avoidance. And you no longer wallow in self-pity. You choose to confront your past trauma or current tormentor. You accept your own limitations and your misfortunes. More important, you accept that suffering is necessary for you to gain valuable knowledge and grow character. With acceptance comes a new sense of freedom and a more realistic assessment of your situation.

(2) Affirmation

You have accepted that your life circumstances could not have been worse. The world seems to be so dark and the future so bleak. Based on your painful experience, you have concluded that most people are selfish and that there is no justice. You have been wondering: What is the point? What is the use of fighting a losing battle? What is the meaning and purpose of suffering?

Yet even while hitting rock bottom, and in the throes of struggling, your eyes are opened to new possibilities. Yes, there is goodness in life, and there is meaning and purpose in

(*continued*)

(*continued*)

suffering. You choose to take a positive stance, because this is the only way out of the dark pit; the alternative to affirmation is self-destruction and death. You affirm meaning, because there is no future without believing that there is something worth living for.

By affirming life, you begin to appreciate all the little things you used to take for granted. You learn to delight in the natural beauty around you and the simple pleasures of life. Yes, it is exciting to be alive. It is worth fighting for.

(3) Determination

Once you have chosen to embark on the road of recovery, you know that it will require perseverance and determination to make progress. Once you have started your quest for meaning and authenticity, you know that there will be obstacles, opposition, and even dangers. Yes, you are prepared to persist with courage and tenacity. Even if you may never arrive at the Promised Land, to be able to strive toward a worthy goal is enough to fill your heart with deep satisfaction.

(4) Confidence

You have been feeling helpless and powerless. You have been saying, "I can't go on anymore. I am finished. There is nothing left in me. Life has run over me like a 5-ton truck and left me dying."

But with affirmation and determination, your confidence gradually returns. With every small victory, your confidence grows. Now you say to yourself: "If I can survive this, I can survive anything. I know that the forces of evil are still there, and the obstacles are still there. The difficulties are formidable, but not insurmountable. Yes, I CAN overcome with God's help and support from others."

(*continued*)

(*continued*)

Your confidence is no longer solely based on your own ability. Paradoxically, you have regained a sense of confidence and control through accepting your vulnerability and surrendering to someone much stronger than yourself.

(5) Religious Faith

You have been wondering whether God listens to your prayers and whether He really cares. Like Job in the Old Testament, you have complained bitterly about God's indifference to your misfortunes. But now the fog has lifted, and you realize that God is with you, crying with you and sharing your pain throughout your struggles. He does not shield you from suffering, but He gives you the grace to endure and learn. You begin to hear God's reassuring whisper and experience His tender embrace when you are feeling all alone and trembling with fear. Now you can rebuild your life on the solid rock of faith.

(6) Relationships

You used to be preoccupied with your own needs. You used to feel sorry for yourself. But now your eyes are open to all those who suffer more than you do. You begin to seek out opportunities to help others. You discover that in helping others, you find healing for yourself.

Your priorities have changed. Now your family and friends become more important than your personal achievements. Their support and care have nurtured you back to health. Now you learn to appreciate and enjoy them in a way unknown to you before the traumatic event. You have grown in relationships as a result of the trauma.

(7) Optimism

At long last, you can hope again. Born of adversity and baptized by trauma, your hope will be able to endure anything that may come your way. You can now talk about your future

(*continued*)

(*continued*)

with excitement, even though you know that danger may be lurking just around the corner. Your tragic sense of life is now married to a positive outlook in life, resulting in a mature tragic optimism.

Conclusion

I have provided a roadmap that extends beyond the traditional psychological territory of self-efficacy and internal locus of control. I have shown pathways to growth that go beyond traditional modalities of treating PTSD. Like tragic optimism, PTG is yet another example of the kind of mature positive psychology that resonates with all individuals who are going through suffering, pain, and despair.

Source: Wong (2003). International Network on Personal Meaning. www.meaning.ca. Used with permission.

CONCLUSION

Although triumph after tragedy has been described since ancient times, the academic study of PTG is relatively new. These recent studies document that the results of traumatic events do not have to be all bad. Good can come from devastating circumstances or the evil intentions of others. These studies indicate that growth is not cheap but in fact often comes with a high price tag. But ultimately the literature on PTG provides hope to people who have experienced devastating life events: hope that they can potentially come out on the other side and be different—better—than they were before. Lucie describes the importance of this work to trauma survivors:

The area of posttraumatic growth is extraordinarily close to my heart, and I feel incredibly blessed to know deeply how important and restorative and healing it is. I would love to share with you how I've come to feel that way, if for no other reason than to put into circulation a story someone like me could identify with, because when I was in the thick of my own trauma and PTSD that came after, I searched high and low, craving some glimmer of kinship with someone, anyone, whose constellation of events/experiences was like mine, and while I did find a lot of stories that did help me, I still to this day have never come across any I read and thought, "Oh yeah, that's totally me!" Plus, looking back, when I think of all of the junctures where seeing a story like mine might have clued me in a little earlier to what I was in, I'm pretty confident that would have made a huge difference for me. In short, I see sharing my story as a huge public service.

REFERENCES

Anderson, K. M., Renner, L. M., & Danis, F. S. (2012). Recovery: Resilience and growth in the aftermath of domestic violence. *Violence Against Women, 18*(1), 1279–1299.

Blix, I., Hansen, M. B., Birkeland, M. S., Nissen, A., & Heir, T. (2013). Posttraumatic growth, posttraumatic stress and psychological adjustment in the aftermath of the 2011 Oslo bombing attack. *Health and Quality of Life Outcomes, 11*, 160.

Chan, C. S., & Rhodes, J. E. (2013). Religious coping, posttraumatic stress, psychological distress, and posttraumatic growth among female survivors four years after Hurricane Katrina. *Journal of Traumatic Stress, 26*, 257–265.

Duran, B. (2013). Posttraumatic growth as experienced by childhood cancer survivors and their families: A narrative synthesis of qualitative and quantitative research. *Journal of Pediatric Oncology Nursing, 30*(4), 179–197. doi:10.1177/1043454213487433

Glad, K. A., Jensen, T. K., Holt, T., & Ormhaug, S. M. (2013). Exploring self-perceived growth in a clinical sample of severely traumatized youth. *Child Abuse & Neglect, 37*, 331–342.

Janoff-Bulman, R. (1992). *Shattered assumptions: Towards a new psychology of trauma.* New York, NY: The Free Press.

Joseph, S. (2011). *What doesn't kill us: The new psychology of posttraumatic growth.* New York, NY: Basic Books.

Koutrouli, N., Anagnostopoulos, F., & Potamianos, G. (2012). Posttraumatic stress disorder and posttraumatic growth in breast cancer patients: A systematic review. *Women & Health, 52*(5), 503–516.

Levine, S. Z., Laufer, A., Stein, E., Hamama-Raz, Y., & Solomon, Z. (2009). Examining the relationship between resilience and posttraumatic growth. *Journal of Traumatic Stress, 22*(4), 282–286.

Meyerson, D. A., Grant, K. E., Carter, J. S., & Kilmer, R. P. (2011). Posttraumatic growth among children and adolescents: A systematic review. *Clinical Psychology Review, 31*, 949–964.

Tedeschi, R. G., & Calhoun, L. G. (1996). The Posttraumatic Growth Inventory: Measuring the positive legacy of trauma. *Journal of Traumatic Stress, 9*, 455–471.

Tedeschi, R. G., & Calhoun, L. G. (2004). Posttraumatic growth: Conceptual foundations and empirical evidence. *Psychological Inquiry, 15*(1), 1–18.

Tedeschi, R. G., & McNally, R. J. (2011). Can we facilitate posttraumatic growth in combat veterans? *American Psychologist, 66*(1), 19–24.

Teodorescu, D.-S., Siqveland, J., Heir, T., Hauff, E., Wentzel-Larsen, T., & Lien, L. (2012). Posttraumatic growth, depressive symptoms, posttraumatic stress symptoms, post-migration stressors and quality of life in multi-traumatized psychiatric outpatients with a refugee background in Norway. *Health and Quality of Life Outcomes, 10*, 84.

Wong, P. T. P. (2003). *Pathways to posttraumatic growth.* Retrieved from http://www.meaning.ca/archives/presidents_columns/pres_col_may_2003_post-traumatic-growth.htm

Index

CPSIA information can be obtained
at www.ICGtesting.com
Printed in the USA
BVHW030849200722
642565BV00014B/304